CONQUERORS OF YELLOW FEVER
(by Dean Cornwell, N.A.)

MEMOIR OF WALTER REED

The Yellow Fever Episode

By

ALBERT E. TRUBY

Brigadier General,
United States Army, Retired

PAUL B. HOEBER, INC.

MEDICAL BOOK DEPARTMENT OF HARPER & BROTHERS

NEW YORK   LONDON

FOREWORD

YELLOW fever, which is now believed to have come to us from Africa with the slave trade, has been always a thing of mystery, tragedy, and dread. The whimsical way in which it spread gave rise constantly to new theories as to its cause and prevention, each of which was soon upset by other observations. The theory of its transmission by a variety of mosquito was published in 1881 by Dr. Carlos J. Finlay of Havana, but it made no converts in nineteen years although it was stoutly maintained by Dr. Finlay in many publications both in Spanish and English. True to the record of yellow fever for the unusual, his theory after so many years of incredulity, upon its verification by the Reed Board, was accepted by all the world. The brilliant clarity of Reed's carefully controlled experiments, made on human subjects who volunteered from a love for humanity and also probably from a spirit of adventure; the tragic death of Lazear; the prompt acceptance of the Finlay theory after its demonstration by the Reed Board, all constitute a dramatic episode without precedent in medical history. It has so intrigued the popular imagination that doctors, teachers, playwrights, newspapermen, magazine writers, and artists, have kept alive interest during more than forty years. Many errors, misunderstandings, and partisan statements have become current during that time, some of which have shown great tenacity of life. Several years ago, by a fortunate incident, a born investigator, Dr. Philip S. Hench, of the Mayo Clinic, became interested, first in the work of Dr. Jesse W. Lazear as a member of the Yellow Fever Board and finally in the whole episode and all the individuals concerned therewith. Captivated by the moving features of this historical work, Dr. Hench, though a very busy man as an author, editor, and member of the Clinic, has done a vast amount of research work which has taken him twice to Cuba, many times to Washington and to every part of the country where he could interview a survivor of the brave men who volunteered for the famous experiments. His objective was to clear up all doubtful or disputed points, to evaluate, as far as possible, the part played by each of the chief actors and to make an authentic and factual history of the great demonstration. His tireless pursuit of details had a stimulating influence on all who met him and underwent his categorical inquisitions. General Truby and I have had to study many old papers and furbish up old memories of our service in Cuba in 1900 at his request.

Brigadier General Albert E. Truby, U.S.A., when he retired for age in 1935, had completed thirty-seven years of active service in Cuba, the Philippines, Panama, and the four quarters of the United States. This is not the place, nor have we the space to mention the various interesting duties of his long and most creditable career. It may fairly be said, however, that he had performed efficiently the duties of each grade from lieutenant to brigadier general before the promotion to such grade came to him. General Truby was assembling his data and putting on paper his reminiscences before the added stimulus of Dr. Hench's researches came to him. The end result has been this memoir which has delighted those who have had the privilege of reading it in manuscript. The charming story of his experience before the Army Medical Examining Board of 1898 is especially pleasing to the old timers of the Medical Corps who are proudly reminiscent of surviving this ordeal, which served a good purpose in its day, but has now fortunately been replaced by a better and less painful method of selection.

It was fortunate that when Reed and Carroll landed in Cuba in June 1900, and came to live at the post hospital of Columbia Barracks, Reed should find

Lieutenant Truby, for whom he had a high regard, on duty there as Executive Officer and at times in charge of the hospital. He saw Truby constantly at the medical officers' mess and was able to make use of his knowledge in many ways, and especially of Truby's acquaintance with the characters and qualifications of the enlisted men of the Hospital Corps who later were to furnish his most valuable volunteers for the famous experiments. As Columbia Barracks was under rigid military quarantine against yellow fever and its commanding officer was known to be a parlous person, the members of the Board were wisely reticent as to their work, and Lieutenant Truby had more intimate knowledge of what was being done than anyone else in Cuba. So closely was he in touch with their work that Reed desired to take him as a member of the Board in Lazear's place, but this was not done because Truby was suddenly sent to the south coast where conditions had arisen which called for the qualities of efficiency and good judgment that his superiors knew him to possess. Therefore this memoir is a precious source of inside information and rarely do we find a story of personal experience told so modestly and with such intrinsic charm.

JEFFERSON RANDOLPH KEAN

Washington, D. C.

PREFACE

THIS is a story of my early professional life when by good fortune I was immediately launched into the midst of great historical events and among medical men whose names were to become famous throughout the world. The greatest of these events was the conquest of yellow fever, and the man to become most famous was Walter Reed, an Army surgeon. When Major Walter Reed and the members of his Board were conducting their history-making experiments at the hospital, Columbia Barracks, Cuba, in 1900, I happened to be one of the Army doctors on duty there.

In recent years, public interest in that great yellow fever episode has developed enormously. Unfortunately, but quite naturally, some distortion of the facts has crept into the picture. Because of that and the fact that many details of the work and incidents connected with it have never been told, I have repeatedly been urged to write what I know of the personnel, the work they did, their living conditions, and the scene in general.

About three years ago, I began collecting and assorting my old records with a view to writing a brief autobiography for record purposes. The probable historical value of my information about the occupation of Cuba by our troops and the work at Columbia Barracks convinced me that I was in duty bound to place on record what I knew of that eventful period. There are facts which have never been published, and some that have been published require elucidation.

In order to qualify as a writer of such important historical events, some of which have been the subject of a bitter controversy, it seemed best to expand that part of my memoir explaining my entrance into the scene, the conditions found in Havana, the work of the Reed Board and how Walter Reed lived and worked with a group of young doctors.

In recounting an experience of this kind, it must of course be made as factual as possible if it is to have historical value. Every effort has therefore been made to insure accuracy, although memory of many incidents could be supported only by calling to my assistance the memory and records of others who were in Cuba with me at that time. I have therefore had an extensive correspondence with them, had them review the manuscript, and give their version of details which were not too clear in my own mind. The results have been very gratifying and have been quoted freely in the text. I am confident that many significant details, not covered in official reports, have in this way been brought to light, and they are in my opinion reliable. The opportunity for this extensive and interesting correspondence with former associates has been one of the most pleasant features of the work. My sincere appreciation for their valuable assistance is extended to all of them, expecially to Brigadier General J. R. Kean, Dr. A. S. Pinto, Mr. Gustav Lambert, and the following heroic participants in the yellow fever experiments in Cuba, whose names are inscribed on the "Congressional Roll of Honor": John H. Andrus, John R. Kissinger, James L. Hanberry, Clyde L. West, and Thomas M. England.

While working on the preliminary draft of the manuscript, Dr. Philip S. Hench greatly stimulated my efforts by his enthusiastic search for information on the subject. The voluminous correspondence which followed during the next two years was most helpful. I am deeply indebted to him, not only for the inspiration he gave me, but for his co-operation and help in many ways.

Walter Reed's letter of December 9, 1900 written to Mrs. Reed, and first published in 1906 by Dr. Howard A. Kelly in his book "Walter Reed and Yellow Fever," and five of Walter Reed's letters to General Sternberg, which were first published in a

"Biography of George Miller Sternberg," in 1920 by
the American Medical Association, have been quoted
by permission of Dr. Kelly and of Dr. Morris Fishbein,
secretary of the Association, respectively. Their courtesy is much appreciated.

A. E. T.

San Francisco, California

CONTENTS

MEMOIR OF WALTER REED

The Yellow Fever Episode

CHAPTER ONE

MEETING WALTER REED

AT THE beginning of the year 1898, I was a resi-dent physician at the University of Pennsylvania Hospital. I was the senior resident on the surgical service with the professor of surgery at the University, Dr. John Ashhurst, Jr., as my chief. It was an active service and very valuable to the residents as we always assisted our great chief in the surgical clinics as well as in all other operations.

The destruction of the battleship *Maine* in Havana harbor, and the subsequent declaration of war against Spain, caused much excitement. As the local troops from Philadelphia began to depart for the front, my young confrères and I all developed the war fever and were anxious to do our part. My service at the hospital would be over in a short time. I was full of youthful enthusiasm for action and I felt that medical service with troops would be valuable as well as thrilling.

Just as I was beginning to make inquiries about the Army, Dr. Ira A. Shimer, a classmate, came to our hospital and told us that he had just returned from

Washington where he had successfully taken the examination for a commission in the Medical Department of the Army. This was in the latter part of May and you may be sure we were keen to get all the information he could give us. He told us that a letter to the Surgeon General, accompanied by letters of recommendation "from two physicians *in good standing* in the profession," would probably bring us the necessary authority to take the examination. Dr. Shimer advised applying at once as nearly all the vacancies in the corps had been filled. The scope of the examination included non-medical subjects such as history, literature, chemistry, physics, even though the candidate was a college graduate. This was discouraging and none of my friends at the hospital or at "Blockley" would take a chance without time to prepare. However, it seemed advisable for me to make an application. A prompt, favorable reply was hardly expected, but it came by return mail. It authorized me to report to the president of the examining board in Washington at 9 A.M. on the following Monday.

Dr. Ashhurst came to the hospital at 12 noon daily. It was my duty to meet him at the front door and then make the rounds of the hospital with him. He had been a surgeon in the Army during the Civil War and I wanted his advice. So, as we proceeded along the corridors, I told him the story. He made no comment but when I said that two of the residents had given me letters of recommendation, he looked at me with a glance that I shall never forget. After finishing his work in the wards, he took me to the hospital office and gave me a heart-to-heart talk. He warned me that the service examinations were very thorough and that I should not be too optimistic. On the other hand, he advised me to take the examination as "the experience will be valuable to you." Referring to the two letters of recommendation, he said:

"Will you not be somewhat embarrassed if you are asked about the doctors who indorsed you? I suggest that you take along two additional letters from older men in the profession. If you like, I will bring you one tomorrow."

This was, I knew, a most unusual thing for him to do. He either admired my nerve or took pity on my ignorance. With bolstered courage, I lost no time in getting to the office of the professor of medicine, Dr. William Pepper. He had been my chief on the medical service of the hospital. As usual, he was very busy but saw me and expressed his approval of my desire to enter the Service. I left there with another real letter.

On Sunday afternoon—it was early in June—I took the train for Washington. The next morning, long before the appointed time, I found myself in the empty corridors of the Army Medical Museum and Library building at Seventh and B Streets, S. W. A group of twenty young men soon collected. It was a peculiar gathering of men, representing all sections of the country, dressed in garbs quite as characteristic and strange. Some wore the formal clothing of the typical politician of that day—Prince Albert coat with a broad-brimmed black felt hat. A ten gallon hat was also conspicuous. On this sizzling hot day in Washington, those of us from the Eastern Seaboard were decidedly more at ease in light summer suits.

In spite of the existing tension, one candidate amused us by appearing with a black leather grip which everyone recognized. It was a standard obstetrical bag of that period, converted in this instance into a container for medical literature (quiz books, etc.). A few of the leaders in the joshing seemed to know the young "Doc," but it was plainly evident that they and most of the other candidates were nervous. One big fellow in a frock coat, who hailed from the Middle West, seemed to be an exception. He seemed to be most confident as he proudly displayed letters from the governor of his state, the mayor of his city, and two United States senators. He predicted that those of us without political backing would have little chance of success.

Promptly at 9 A.M., a dapper-looking, tall young officer in a captain's uniform appeared and conducted the group to the board room. He was the junior member of the board and its recorder. The other members (all in blue dress uniforms) were seated around a large table. They were all strangers to me, as were all of the candidates. The preliminary proceedings were formal, according to Army custom, and left a lasting impression on the candidates. The president outlined the procedure and gave us instructions. Finally he told us that the board would examine first on the professional subjects, and that the test on the elementary branches would come at the end of the week. We were to be called alphabetically for the oral examinations each afternoon. Written examinations would take up the morning hours.

The physical examination was then started. As my name was at the end of the list, I was the last to be called. They went over me with meticulous care. I was then told to be back in the afternoon for the oral examination in anatomy. The question of submitting my additional letters was never out of mind and I decided that this was the time to end the suspense. So, still stripped, I stated that I had two additional letters of recommendation to submit. One of the members, a very large man, had my papers in his hands. He said: "I notice that these letters with your application both come from 3400 Spruce Street. That is the university hospital, is it not?"

So the whole matter came out in all its details and the board saw the humorous side of it—much to my peace of mind. While I was dressing, the two letters I had just presented were being read, and I realized their value to me.

I spent a trying afternoon standing in the inhospitable corridor or sitting on the front steps of the building, awaiting my turn at the oral examination in anatomy. Six candidates had failed in the physical test that morning, and now the gloom thickened as it soon became evident that this anatomy test was creating havoc in our ranks. The big fellow with all the "pull" headed straight for the front door after his examination without a word of comment and we saw no more of him. It was very late in the afternoon when my turn came. The large officer previously mentioned was conducting the examination. The questions came at me with great speed and if he saw that I knew the answer, the next question came before I could finish the one in hand. He reminded me of a famous old quiz master at the university, "Dave" Birney, in size as well as in his knowledge of the subject. The examiner was hot and tired and stern. After about a half hour, he relaxed, sat back in his chair and with a grand, whole-hearted smile, said: "Come back in the morning, Doctor."

As I arose to leave, Major Arthur introduced himself and said that during the past year he had been on duty in Philadelphia and on Saturdays had attended Dr. Ashhurst's clinics where he had observed my work. Referring to the letters which I had submitted, he remarked: "I was pleased to see the letter from your chief."

His friendly attitude led me to ask him about the elementary subjects which were slated for the end of the week. I told him that I had had no time to prepare for the examination. He suggested that I go to the second-hand book store near Seventh and "the Avenue" and obtain books on history, literature, chemistry and physics, and "burn a little midnight oil." I promptly acquired familiar old books and really went to work. I not only burned midnight oil but always had one of the books with me for study while awaiting my turn at the examinations.

On Tuesday afternoon but seven candidates appeared. Six had failed the physical examination, and seven had failed in anatomy. Others fell down in surgery; and then on Wednesday afternoon came the oral examination in medicine.

A tall, slender officer, very military in appearance,

with a serious but kindly face, then took us in hand. It was Major Walter Reed. I had never heard of him. He conducted us to his laboratory in the Army Medical School, on an upper floor of the same building, and gave each of us prepared slides to identify under the microscope. The slides were numbered and we were told to make a list of our findings. I soon found that they contained nicely stained specimens of the common pathogenic bacteria; stained and unstained smears of blood, with and without malarial parasites; also a few histological and pathological sections for diagnosis. This was one subject on which I *knew* the answers (except for the sections in pathology) for reasons which will soon be related. I finished first and took my answers to the Major. He said: "Don't hurry, Doctor."

He glanced at the list and then said: "Well! We can start the oral examination in medicine."

He left the other candidates with an assistant in the laboratory who was, as I later learned, Dr. James Carroll, and we went to his office down the hall. He started out gently on this broad subject of medicine with general questions, giving me the responsibility of selecting and discussing the salient points. Occasionally he would interrupt to bring out some particular point. He made me feel at ease and it was clear that he was endeavoring to find out how well-grounded the candidates were and if they were abreast of *recent progress* in medicine. An example of this is still fresh in my memory. He asked me to discuss the etiology of malaria. By sheer good luck, I had seen in one of our medical journals that Ronald Ross, a British scientist, had quite recently proved that certain mosquitoes transmitted malaria. From his reaction to my answer, it was clear that this was what he wanted, for he promptly went on to another subject. This was the only time during the examination, however, that I really was able to fathom his reaction. I was attracted by his courteous and gentle manner as well as his way of conducting the examination. It was evident that he was experienced as a teacher, knew his subject, and would, also, I thought, be fair in judging my qualifications. He gave me much confidence.

When he finished the oral examination, he looked over the answers I had submitted in the laboratory test. He was deeply interested he said, in finding out how much practical laboratory work in bacteriology was given in our medical schools. I explained that the practical course in laboratory work in my school was very brief but that a very comprehensive course in bacteriology was given in the university's department of hygiene, under Dr. A. C. Abbott.* I also explained

* A few years later, Dr. Abbott gave such a course in the medical school of the university.

that during my senior year in college, before entering the medical school, I had taken that course and for a full year had worked directly under Dr. Abbott and Dr. Mazyck P. Ravanel, one of the instructors.*

The Major was plainly interested in Dr. Abbott's course and asked several questions about the work done there. I did not learn until 1900 that Reed and Abbott were close friends, having worked together in Professor Welch's laboratory at Johns Hopkins.

On Thursday afternoon, the examination on the elementary subjects began, with Major Merrill conducting. I felt that I had probably passed the professional subjects by a scant margin and that everything now hinged on things I had once known but probably had forgotten. There was but *one* other candidate left and our morale was not too good. We had a trying afternoon and a still worse day on Friday, but both of us were told to be back at 9 o'clock on Saturday morning. That was reassuring but—what was coming next? We did not know.

Captain A. N. Stark, the recorder of the board, met

* At the end of my junior year at Cornell University, I decided to study medicine and, because it seemed advantageous to take my senior year where I could also attend medical lectures and clinics, I transferred to the University of Pennsylvania. Dr. Horace Jayne, dean of the college department, outlined my course and to him I was indebted for taking Dr. Abbott's course. The only other student in the class was W. F. Truby, a cousin of mine. Capt. George H. Torney of the Medical Corps of the Army took the course with us during the spring months of 1894. He became Surgeon General of the Army in 1909.

us and we were taken to the Garfield Hospital. In one of the wards for chronically ill patients, two patients were assigned to me for diagnosis by physical signs alone. Once again I felt at home and soon reported my findings. On our way back, Captain Stark told us that the Board would hold a meeting at 11 o'clock and that the results would then be announced.

By this time I knew the names and rank of the members of the board:

Colonel Dallas Bache, President
Major Walter Reed
Major J. C. Merrill
Major W. H. Arthur
Captain A. N. Stark, Recorder.

I was called before them, again in formal session, and told by the president that I would be recommended to the Surgeon General for a commission in the Medical Department of the Army and that at 2 P.M. Captain Stark would take us (the two successful candidates) to the War Department to meet the Surgeon General.

General Sternberg received us, and although his office was a very busy place, he devoted considerable time to explaining the medical service. He also said that there were but two more vacancies to be filled.*

* Congress in 1894 had reduced the strength of the Medical Corps from 192 to 177. On May 12, 1898 it restored the 15 so lost, and the vacancies were then being filled in the manner

General Sternberg said that it would be about a month before we would receive our commissions and orders for duty. He also said that if we wanted to be put to work at once, he would be glad to employ us under the contract system at a salary of $150 a month. As I still had about a month to serve at my hospital, I declined.

I left the Surgeon General's office in the old State War and Navy building with mixed feelings. I was elated and yet perplexed. Had I taken this important step in my early professional life with wisdom? I had, at that time, no intention of remaining permanently in the Service.

On my way back to Philadelphia that afternoon, I did, however, get a "big kick" in contemplating the surprise I had in store for my friends at the hospital. An impromptu "pink tea" was staged for me that evening in the residents' quarters. At noon on Sunday I was at the door to meet Dr. Ashhurst. His reception of me is one of my most pleasant memories.

The commonplace experience herein related has been included since it tells of my first meeting with Walter Reed, the kindly and truly great man who will

---

described. With this small corps, the number of vacancies each year was very small and the number of applicants for those vacancies very large. Consequently a high standard had been set years before and this was then and still is being maintained.

figure so largely in the rest of the story. Major Arthur and Captain Stark also became lifelong friends of mine. It also explains how the officers of the Medical Department of the Army were selected.

CHAPTER TWO

ACTIVE ARMY SERVICE—HAVANA

I WAS commissioned in the Medical Department on July 23, 1898, and assigned to duty at Fort Myer, Virginia. The regular garrison of the post was absent at Santiago, Cuba, and all the large buildings, including barracks and riding hall, were now utilized as wards of a general hospital with a capacity of about five hundred beds. The hospital was constantly filled with typhoid fever cases from various camps including Camp Alger, Virginia, and later on from Montauk Point, New York.

The entire medical personnel—doctors, women nurses, and members of the hospital corps—were overworked. Hemorrhages, perforations, and other complications of this terrible disease were constantly taking place with about the normal civilian death rate. Specialists, such as Woodbridge and Brand, tried out their special treatments in wards assigned to them, while the rest of the staff followed the treatment outlined by Osler. It was, from a professional standpoint,

Albert E. Truby

1905.

Fig. 1. Albert E. Truby.

FIG. 2. Riding hall, Fort Myer, Virginia, September 1898. This photograph was taken when the hall was open for patients. The commanding officer, Major William B. Davis, Medical Corps, stands in the central aisle. The hall was cubicled into sections later. (From Annual Report of the Surgeon General.)

a very interesting and valuable experience; but from any other angle a terrible one.

On October 3, 1898, an unexpected order came for me to report to the Commanding Officer, Eighth United States Infantry at Huntsville, Alabama, as Regimental Surgeon. This regiment had just arrived there from Montauk Point after the hard campaign at Santiago, Cuba. The troops were riddled with malaria and typhoid, several of such cases being admitted to the hospital daily. Acting Assistant Surgeon (Contract Surgeon) W. N. Bispham was my assistant and the detachment consisted of an acting hospital steward and fifteen men. The tent hospital of sixteen beds was satisfactory as all serious cases were promptly transferred to the better equipped brigade hospital for definitive treatment.

The regiment was camped in a cottonfield at the foot of a very high hill with steep slopes. Fall rains had been heavy and the seepage of water at the foot of this mountain kept the camp a virtual mud puddle during most of our time there. Latrines were often flooded and it was the most unsanitary, cold, and uncomfortable camp imaginable. Recruits to fill vacancies caused by losses at Santiago came in large numbers. Most of these young, untrained men soon developed typhoid and thus our morbidity and mortality rates constantly increased.

Orders came early in December, 1898, for the regiment to proceed to Havana, Cuba. On December 10, we broke camp and left Huntsville by train for Tampa, Florida. Headquarters and the First Battalion sailed from Tampa on December 13, on a very small passenger steamer, the S.S. *Florida*. The remainder of the regiment, including Dr. Bispham, embarked on another steamer, a side-wheeler.

We entered Havana harbor shortly before sunrise on the morning of December 14, 1898. Everyone was on deck on this beautiful morning, eagerly taking in the gorgeous spectacle before us. On our left was the famous Morro Castle; just beyond, the enormous Cabaña Fortress. The top walls of the latter of these two great fortresses were lined with Spanish troops viewing the peaceful * entrance of one of the first ships carrying United States troops. On our right (west) La Punta—a small, old, stone fort—and Havana with its tinted buildings made an impressive sight.

Along the sea wall, thousands of natives had gathered to see us. There was no excitement but evidently great curiosity. I doubt, however, if their curiosity and interest in the passing show was as great as that of the officers and men on the S.S. *Florida*. The experi-

* All fighting in Cuba took place on land and sea near Santiago, in the spring of 1898, and all claims to Cuba were surrendered by Spain in the preliminary peace treaty the following August.

ence of our troops at Santiago and the extensive publicity given about everything concerning Cuba had prepared us for almost anything. I was well up in the medical history of Havana and realized that I had a man's job with about 1,000 non-immune men under my care. Of course all this responsibility and the grave history of the place should have weighed heavily but I doubt if it gave me any anxiety as we passed up to our mooring place that morning. The gorgeousness of the setting, the historical events that were taking place, and the fact that I was present to play my part seemed to banish anxiety about the future troubles all of us expected to have.

A sanitary order for the command, based on such knowledge as we had regarding tropical diseases (especially yellow fever) had been published. Therefore we had to await developments. They came slowly but surely, yet were never so bad as to disrupt the military machine. An English force had been practically wiped out in and around Havana by sickness. Havard, writing of yellow fever, says:

This disease caused fearful loss of life in all the military expeditions to the West Indies during the past two centuries, and compelled the English, after their conquest of Havana in 1763, to return that city to the Spaniards in exchange for Florida.[1]

[1] Havard: Military Hygiene. Ed. 3, 1917, page 73.

Quoting Sternberg:

In 1779 there arrived from Spain, then at war with Great Britain, "an army of 3,500 men, which was immediately decimated by the vomito." In 1780 during the month of August, an army of 8,000 men was landed in Havana, which during the two following months suffered a loss of about 2,000 men with the vomito. Pezuela records the fact that in 1794, in the garrison and squadron there were more than 1,600 victims of the disease.[2]

Since that time the medical profession, while it knew absolutely nothing about the etiology of yellow fever, had learned that if the disease got started in a command, it was possible to move the command away from it. Very soon, too, we were to learn from Walter Reed and the members of his board that a common domestic mosquito of tropical and subtropical countries was responsible for transmitting the disease. So "The crowning medical discovery of the Nineteenth Century came just at its close" to help us out.

The S.S. *Florida* came to anchor near the wreck of the *Maine* and we had a close view of some of her superstructure and masts as they protruded above the surface of the bay. After a short delay, we proceeded to one of the large docks. When our ship tied up at

[2] Sternberg, G. M.: Researches Relating to the Etiology and Prevention of Yellow Fever. Document No. 1328, Marine Hospital Service, page 39.

FIG. 3. View of La Punta and Morro Castle from the sea wall looking out over the entrance to Havana harbor. Only the modern parapet of La Punta is shown. Note the four tents of the staff.

FIG. 4. Departure of the Spanish Governor General and last Spanish troops from Havana in the afternoon of January 1, 1899. Note the Stars and Stripes on Morro Castle and the Spanish flag on the transport. The photograph was taken by the author from his tent at La Punta.

the dock, we were met by a lone officer of the Quartermaster Department. He was Captain Chauncey B. Baker and he seemed most active and efficient. In a well-fitting khaki uniform made in Havana, he looked most comfortable to us who were garbed in woolen uniforms more suitable for Alaska than for Cuba. Baker was in charge of everything, being the only officer (excepting those with the Peace Commission) on duty in Havana at that time.

From him, we learned that we were the first Regular Army troops to arrive and land at Havana. Captain Baker had succeeded Colonel Williams, Quartermaster Corps, who with Colonel Waring, a noted sanitary expert from New York City, had been sent to Havana in August 1898, to make plans for the landing of troops. Both of these officers and several of their clerical assistants had promptly contracted yellow fever and died. Baker succeeded Williams.

Later on, the ship with the remainder of the regiment arrived. Other transports were also entering the harbor while we were at the dock and anchored in the bay. Unloading started and continued until the morning of December 15 when the regiment marched from the docks to Quemados, about six miles to the southwest. Captain Baker arranged all details for our camp site, arranged for supplies, and provided a guide to march with us to camp. (See Appendix, I.)

Our command was still in heavy blue uniforms with full field equipment, and the march was a hot one. We passed through the narrow streets of the old city on cobblestone pavements until we reached a broad boulevard leading to Principe Hill, with its fortifications, and not far from Colon Cemetery where the *Maine* dead were interred. The streets were lined with curious people all deeply interested in getting a first glimpse of United States troops. At several points, we passed Spanish barracks and at each place Spanish troops were lined up as we passed. There were no demonstrations of any kind.

At Buena Vista, near Quemados, our guide turned off the main highway to a beautiful camp site on a plateau about one hundred and fifty feet above sea level. The flat area extended about a mile southwestward and was about a half mile wide. The area was covered with short grass and an occasional tree but with no habitations. Later on, this camp site of ours became the northeastern end of Camp Columbia. The view out over the Gulf of Mexico with its beautiful blue waters was most inspiring and even though it was hot in the sun, there was a delightful breeze and the men soon made themselves comfortable.

The regimental tent hospital was established under a long row of royal palm trees on the border of the town, not far from the main highway to Havana.

Fig. 5. Author's tent at La Punta. Morro Castle in background. January 1899.

Fig. 6. The regimental hospital at
La Punta, December 1898.

While these grand trees gave us little or no shade, they were most attractive. Having been traveling almost a week, we had collected a number of sick, not a few of whom had typhoid fever. We evidently could not "run away" from that disease. It was carried right along with us and new recruits from the States continued to bring it with them as long as infected camps existed at home. As our regiment constituted the vanguard of the "Army of Cuban Occupation," no provision had yet been made for the permanent care of such cases so we had to keep them. The contrast with the cold, muddy, unsanitary and otherwise disagreeable camp in the States was so inspiring that the morale of everyone, including the sick, was very high.

The Tenth United States Infantry was the next regular organization to arrive in Havana. In a few days, about December 19, Headquarters and a division of the Seventh Army Corps under the command of General Fitzhugh Lee began to arrive and was camped in our vicinity. Some of these troops had been separated from their medical supplies and so, with the authority of our Commanding Officer, our tent hospital was quickly expanded to temporarily take their serious cases. I began to realize my responsibilities. I was still the senior with no one of my corps higher up to consult. However, with General Lee's large com-

mand (two divisions, Seventh Army Corps), older
and experienced medical officers came and soon had
things well in hand. Among these were Lieutenant
Colonel Louis M. Maus, Corps Chief Surgeon, and
Major J. R. Kean, Chief Surgeon, First Division, both
of the Regular Army. Their Second Division Hospital
also came at about that time.*

A battalion of the Second United States Volunteer
Engineers, Seventh Army Corps arrived in Havana on
November 26 to make a survey and arrangements for
camp sites for that command of about 14,000 officers
and men. The engineers were not camped in our vicinity and I saw nothing of them or any work they may
have done. The Eighth Infantry hauled its own water
from wells in Quemados, dug its own latrines, and
hauled its supplies from Havana. (See Appendix, II.)
On December 21 the regiment was taken up for duty
with the Seventh Corps whose headquarters were then
established a short distance from our camp.

The Eighth Infantry was not destined to remain in
this comfortable and delightful camp for a long period.
Trouble was brewing in Havana where personal
grudges between Spaniards and Cubans were being
settled. On the morning of December 23, we were
marched to Vedado, on the outskirts of Havana, and

* Annual Report of Brigadier General Fitzhugh Lee, August
15, 1899.

in a small vacant lot on the hillside pitched shelter tents. Fortunately we had been able to leave our typhoid cases with the doctors of the Seventh Army Corps whom we had previously assisted. Vedado was the finest and most delightful of Havana's suburbs. Attractive homes with beautiful tropical trees and shrubs covered the hillside which sloped to the shore of the Gulf.

At Huntsville, the Headquarters mess lost the fine colored cook who had served us so faithfully and well. The soldier cook we now had was far from satisfactory, so at Vedado we decided to take our meals at the Trotcha Hotel. At dinner that evening, we found a distinguished gathering of United States Army officers as well as a large number of Spanish officers who were now preparing to depart for Spain. General John P. Wade, president of the Peace Commission, and his staff were among them. Fine wines and excellent meals contributed to make this a most pleasant change from routine. We had Christmas dinner there.

Evidently there were many scores to settle between the Cubans and the departing Spaniards. Every night disturbances occurred in Havana, especially in the hotels, with some loss of life. Spanish troops were still in control but the authorities evidently wanted United States troops on hand. These disturbances increased as the time for departure of the Spanish regime approached and, about December 26, the *Eighth Foot* marched to Havana and was camped on the streets at La Punta at the foot of the Prado. The tents of the regimental hospital were erected on the circle of a small park at La Punta. The Tenth Infantry was camped on the Prado only a short distance from our camp.

Major General John R. Brooke and his staff had arrived in Havana and were preparing to take over the command from the Spanish Governor General Castellanos. The Peace Commission with General Wade representing the United States and General Blanco the Spanish Government had arranged all details for the transfer.

Shortly before noon on January 1, 1899, the two Regular Army Regiments (Eighth and Tenth) on duty in Havana were marched to the park in front of the Governor General's palace. Troops were drawn up in close order with the Americans on one side of the park and the departing Spanish on the other, all facing the palace. Everything was peaceful. Promptly at noon, the ceremonies began with the lowering of the Spanish flag from the palace flagstaff and the raising of the Stars and Stripes, the bands playing the appropriate anthems. Battleships and cruisers in the nearby harbor began a thunderous salute as the officers of the old and new regimes closed the formalities of the occasion on the balcony of the palace. General Blanco, his staff and troops then marched to the nearby wharf and embarked on the waiting ships for Spain. Our command was immediately marched back to its camp at La Punta, about a half mile away. The Seventh Army Corps had a great parade in Havana while these events were taking place.

The colonel of the regiment and his staff had their tents on a modern parapet just east of the old fort at La Punta. They were within twenty feet of the water's edge, at the very entrance to the narrow channel leading to the harbor. Being mounted, I arrived at my tent within a very short time after the ceremonies at the palace concluded and, looking across the channel, saw a large United States flag flying from the flagstaff on Morro Castle where the Spanish flag had been waving for many years until noon of that day. Presently the ships carrying the departing Spanish troops began to pass and I managed to get a good photograph of the last one with General Castellanos and his staff aboard. By this time, troops from the United States were pouring in at all Cuban ports. General John R. Brooke, U. S. A., was the new Governor General of Cuba. These great historical events were most inspiring.

The military set-up is outlined in the accompanying diagram.

DIVISION OF CUBA

Major General J. R. Brooke, Commanding

Colonel R. M. O'Reilly, Chief Surgeon

Dept. of Santiago	Dept. of Puerto Principe	Dept. of Matanzas	Dept. of City of Havana	Dept. of Province of Havana	Dept. of Pinar del Rio
Brig. Gen. Leonard Wood, Commanding			Brig. Gen. Wm. Ludlow, Commanding.	Brig. Gen. Fitzhugh Lee, U. S. V., Commanding	
			Major Wm. C. Gorgas, Chief Surgeon	Lt. Col. J. R. Kean, U. S. V., Chief Surgeon. Hdqrs. near Buena Vista, Quemados	

CHAPTER THREE

THE DEPARTMENT OF HAVANA

THE Department of Havana was commanded by Brigadier General William Ludlow. Major W. C. Gorgas was the Department Surgeon and therefore my immediate superior and medical chief. General Ludlow, who had formerly been in the Army Engineer Corps, placed the Street Cleaning Department and general sanitation of the city under Colonel W. M. Black, his Chief of Engineers, as he considered it more of an engineering job than a medical one. Colonel Black had a medical officer of volunteers, Major Davis, to assist him in medical problems. This scheme resulted in the efficient cleaning of the streets, but Davis met with complications and much opposition in the sanitation of private premises. Black established a plant to make electrozone from sea water, and the streets of the city were frequently flushed with this disinfectant.

As soon as Major Gorgas was established in his office, I was there to see him about my problems, especially the disposition of desperate cases of typhoid

fever which were constantly increasing and over-
crowding the capacity of our small regimental hospital. He assured me that the Army was establishing a
hospital, to be known as "Military Hospital No. 1"
and that it would soon be ready to take patients. He
was very courteous, and kindly encouraged me to
come to him at any time for advice or help. That
meant much to me, you may be sure. At that time I
told him of my commanding officer's intention to
utilize the vacant Spanish barracks but that I had advised against it for the present. He said that an order
was being issued by the Department requiring troops
to remain in tents until further orders. The vacant barracks were: La Punta, Maestranza de Artilleria, Dra-
gones, and Balascoaine, on a street of the same name.

Colonel Robert M. O'Reilly, M. C., came and was
designated the Chief Surgeon of the Division of Cuba.
I was advised to call promptly. I did this with hesitation for I held a colonel of my corps in some awe. The
Colonel was alone in his office which was just being
organized. I fully anticipated that a young "shavetail"
in the corps would not be expected to do more than
pay his respects and then graciously withdraw. On
the contrary, I was most courteously received and kept
there an hour or more describing the camp, condition
of the troops, care of the sick, and the other problems
I was encountering. Colonel O'Reilly became ill and

on August 23 went to the United States on leave,
returning October 5. He remained until November 11 when Colonel Calvin DeWitt, M. C., came
to succeed him. Colonel DeWitt was also relieved because of illness on April 3, 1899 and he was succeeded
by Major Valery Havard. All three of these medical
officers were experienced and very capable. Colonel
O'Reilly became the Surgeon General of the Army
and his administration was marked by very pronounced
progress, especially in the prestige of the Medical
Department.

With the establishment of our Government, there
was plenty of work for the two regiments to do in
Havana. Our camp was comfortable, the men were
busy, restrictions moderate, and the morale was good.
Our military bands played in the parks to large
crowds. There was little or no trouble with the
Cubans.

In the fall and winter months, Havana often feels
the effects of a "Norther." One hit us in January
while the regiment was still in tents. I was awakened
in the middle of the night by a high wind, tents flap-
ping, and waves breaking on the rocks a few feet
away. The wind was accompanied by a pouring rain
and the temperature was falling rapidly. Within an
hour, the officers' tents on the parapet at La Punta
were all down and the waves breaking on the rocks

dashed over the entire area. Each officer salvaged his property and we moved into the quarters of the old fort which had been used by Spanish officers. Fortunately these quarters had been disinfected and prepared for occupancy. The enlisted men were better protected as they were not threatened by the sea. Their tents were securely fastened to the hard roadways by long iron pins, made locally for the purpose, since the standard wooden pins could not be used.

Department Headquarters then authorized us to occupy the Spanish barracks after disinfecting them. Of course we wanted to be sure that the disinfection was thorough but no one knew what agent would be most effective in yellow fever. We took plenty of time to do it effectively and used several strong disinfectants. Each room was tightly closed and sulphur in liberal amounts was burned. The next day the walls, ceilings, floors, and everything inside were sprayed with a strong bichloride of mercury solution. This was done by a powerful two-man pump which would throw a strong stream from a hose nozzle for thirty or more feet. The force of this stream alone would kill such insects as mosquitoes at once. Next, the walls were whitewashed, floors scrubbed, and troops moved in. From January until August these barracks were occupied without a single case of yellow fever developing.

There was a dungeon in the old fort with massive stone walls, without openings except a small door. This made an excellent place for disinfecting bedding and clothing. The hospital bedding, infected clothing of all kinds, including that of men returning from A.W.O.L., were disinfected in this chamber. Sulphur dioxide and formaldehyde gas were usually used. The Medical Department had ample supplies of disinfectants and we used them lavishly. Besides disinfecting the clothing of the men who had been A.W.O.L., the men themselves were placed in strict quarantine for seven days and each day were inspected by Dr. Bispham or me. Naturally this quarantine was irksome and disagreeable for the men, but it greatly reduced unauthorized absences and enabled us to observe men who might bring infection into our barracks.

Colonel George M. Randall of the Infantry, who had been promoted to the regiment, joined in the early spring, succeeding Lieutenant Colonel Philip H. Ellis. He had his staff out riding with him daily in the late afternoons in order to familiarize himself with all parts of the city where details of his command were on duty. My own mount, which I had purchased in Huntsville, Alabama, had developed into a very fine animal and these trips were both instructive and pleasant. Havana was always a constant source of interest and delight to me. Our small cavalcade became well known in the city and usually attracted attention. Likewise, large crowds of Cubans were always on hand to watch the military parades, guard mount, and even the daily drills at La Punta.

The regimental hospital was expanding daily to take care of new cases of typhoid fever and the usual ailments of a soldier, except yellow fever. When things seemed desperate, the hospital ship *Missouri* came and evacuated all of our serious cases. After that, we were able to transfer our patients to the United States Military Hospital No. 1, located on Principe Hill, south of Vedado, where suitable shelter and treatment were available. My greatest responsibility at that time was the prompt diagnosis of the various cases of fever which constantly developed. We had to be on the alert for typhoid fever, malaria, dengue, and yellow fever. Bispham and I had had plenty of experience with the first two but had never seen a case of either of the others. Circular No. 9, Headquarters, Division of Cuba, published certain sanitary instructions of the Surgeon General. The following is an extract from that circular:

Every case of fever should receive prompt attention. If albumen is found in the urine of a patient with fever, it should be considered suspicious [of yellow fever], and he should be placed in an isolated tent. The discharges of patients with fever should always be disinfected at once with a solution of carbolic acid (5 per cent), or of chloride of lime (6 ounces to a gallon of water), or with milk of lime made fresh from quicklime.

Consequently we set aside several tents as a receiving ward for all patients with a temperature. Since malaria was then known to be mosquito-borne, all fever cases were properly screened; every case had a blood examination for malaria; and the urine of all cases was tested for albumen. An early diagnosis was often impossible, but as every fever case was isolated and protected against mosquitoes (of which there were few at La Punta), we removed the menace of infecting the rest of the command with any mosquito-borne diseases. The importance of this work was evident and it was not long before we had a case that was very suspicious of yellow fever. Major Gorgas, our Chief Surgeon, was immediately notified and he lost no time in responding, bringing with him Dr. Carlos Finlay, a distinguished local physician. They went over the case carefully, confirmed our findings of albuminuria, and the absence of malarial parasites. The case was suspicious but it was still too early to make a positive diagnosis. They came again the next morning and again on the third day when it was evident that the case was not yellow fever.

Major Gorgas was the outstanding authority in the Army on yellow fever and that, no doubt, explains why he was present in Havana as Chief Surgeon of that Department. He had had yellow fever himself in 1880 at Fort Brown, Texas, where he was then stationed as a lieutenant in the Medical Corps of the Army. That his responsibilities in Havana were fully realized was shown by his constant vigilance and prompt personal investigation of every suspicious case. Naturally his object was to recognize every case at the earliest possible moment so that it could be removed from camp before starting another focus of infection. He also showed his great qualities by being able to gather around him the best qualified medical men. Some of these were given Volunteer commissions in the Army, some were employed under contract (Contract Surgeons) and others gladly offered advice from purely friendly and professional motives. Major Gorgas, with his gracious ways, could get co-operation from everyone. He met with opposition, however, from some of his chiefs in Cuba and later in Panama.

Dr. Carlos J. Finlay was one of these distinguished friends of our Chief Surgeon. Among others who came with Major Gorgas to see our suspicious cases, I remember Dr. A. Albertini, Major R. F. Echeverria, U. S. V., Dr. J. L. Dueñas, and Dr. Dámaso T. Lainé. Later in the year, Professor Juan Guiteras, a native Cuban, came and was closely associated with Major

Gorgas. The Guiteras family had gone as refugees to the United States after the failure of the Cuban insurrection of 1868, and Juan was educated there. He had become a distinguished physician and teacher at the University of Pennsylvania but returned to Cuba in 1899 after the Spaniards had departed. He was probably the first medical authority to advance the theory that Cuban children were not born immune to yellow fever but acquired immunity by mild, un-recognized attacks in childhood. I knew him very well as he was my professor of pathology, and I was a member of the Juan Guiteras Medical Society of the University of Pennsylvania. Dr. Dueñas later pre-sented me with his book, "Diagnosis of Yellow Fever." Dr. Lainé was a quizmaster in pathology during my time at the University of Pennsylvania.

In addition to those who were practicing medicine in Cuba, there was another group of doctors sent down from the United States as experts. They were all supposed to be immunes who had had experience in epidemics in the Southern states. Some of them, Dr. Roger Post Ames being an outstanding example, were truly expert in the diagnosis and treatment of yellow fever. They rendered most excellent and distinguished service to the Government. There were others, how-ever, who were self-styled "experts" and who were probably unsuccessful practitioners at home or mere adventurers. In time, most of them were eliminated.

Dr. Finlay, born in Cuba, December 3, 1833, of a Scottish father and a French mother, settled in Havana as a young practitioner and became one of the leading authorities on yellow fever. Like Major Gorgas, he was gentle and courteous. Although not large in stature, he was distinguished in appearance with his long white burnside whiskers. It was through his kindness that I saw my first case of yellow fever. On one of his visits to La Punta, he presented me with a reprint of one of his articles in which he stated his belief that the mosquito was the agent that transmitted yellow fever. His Cuban confrères in Havana, Gorgas, and Army surgeons in general did not share his beliefs in the theory. His argument that Vera Cruz, Mexico, had mosquitoes and also yellow fever—while Mexico City at an elevation of 7,435 feet above sea level had neither one—was very convincing, but in spite of much experimenting over a long period of years, he had not been able to prove his theory. Perhaps he had not the facilities required for success in this type of work. However, he deserves much credit for his observations and I feel sure that the medical world has given him such recognition.

The mosquito, which Finlay believed was responsible for the transmission of yellow fever, was very common in Havana. At that time it was known as

"*Culex fasciatus.*" Later it was reclassified and called "*Stegomyia fasciatus,*" and still later "*Aëdes aegypti.*" Our orders required all members of the command to use the mosquito bars furnished by the Government as a protection against malaria. After reading Finlay's reprint, the enforced use of mosquito bars as a protection against the many obscure tropical diseases seemed more important than ever. The health record for our command in Havana, excepting for typhoid fever, was excellent, but how much credit for this should be given to the use of mosquito bars cannot, of course, be estimated. However, the fact remains that the Eighth Infantry had no epidemic of the mosquito-borne diseases (malaria, dengue fever, and yellow fever) while stationed in Havana.

After our first suspicious case in January 1899, it was not long before another one developed which became rather famous as well as exciting. The experts failed to agree on a diagnosis. The patient died and an autopsy followed. This was the case of Private Patrick Smith, Company "B," Eighth Infantry (Captain Chase W. Kennedy, Commanding). He was admitted to the regimental hospital at La Punta on February 5, 1899 and died on February 14. This man had served through the Santiago campaign with his company, had contracted malaria at that time and had had a recurrent attack after the regiment arrived in Havana. On this admission, however, he early developed albuminuria and, as usual, the case was promptly reported as suspicious of yellow fever. Gorgas, Finlay, and several other prominent physicians came to see the patient.

Dr. Sanarelli, an Italian working in South America in 1897, had reported his bacillus *"Icteroides"* as the specific agent in yellow fever. Several workers in the United States, including Wasdin and Geddings of the Marine Hospital Service, confirmed his claims. Others including Reed, Carroll, and Agramonte, working with the same organism, did not obtain the same results and came to other conclusions. This great international debate was going on at the time, and Wasdin and Geddings were in Havana concluding their investigation. They heard of my case (Patrick Smith) and asked permission to come and make blood cultures. They promptly reported their findings to Major Gorgas and to me as a positive case of yellow fever, having found the Sanarelli organism in the blood. As the patient's illness progressed, Gorgas, Finlay, and others were quite positive that it was not yellow fever.

At the autopsy which was performed by Dr. Agramonte from the Department Laboratory at Military Hospital No. 1, there were at least a dozen distinguished men present. Among them were Gorgas,

Finlay, Wasdin, and Geddings. Bispham and I were also present. Ulcerated lesions in the ileum (Peyer's patches) and all the other signs pertaining to the classical picture of typhoid were found. The autopsy surgeon reported the cause of death as typhoid fever and all present except Wasdin concurred. I believe that Dr. Geddings did not express his opinion. In my official report to the Surgeon General of the Army, the cause of death was given as typhoid fever.

The Wasdin and Geddings report on the cause of yellow fever was submitted to the Chief of the Marine Hospital Service in the summer of 1899.[3] They fully supported Sanarelli's claims, having found his bacillus in thirteen of the fourteen cases of yellow fever investigated by them in Havana. Patrick Smith's case was one of the thirteen listed and described as yellow fever. In the fall of 1918, when Major General Gorgas was Surgeon General of the Army, it was my good fortune to be on duty in his office. When he had time to relax, he enjoyed reminiscing about our early service in Havana and about this case in particular.

One morning early in May 1899, I was surprised by a visitor from the States. It was Major Walter Reed who had just arrived in Havana. He was espe-

[3] Report of the Commission of Medical Officers detailed by the authority of the President to investigate the cause of yellow fever. (Report through the Surgeon General, Marine Hospital Service, 1899, to the Secretary of the Treasury.)

cially interested in what he had heard concerning the
case of Patrick Smith. I gave him the details and he
also went over our records of the case very carefully.
Reed and Carroll had already determined, to their
satisfaction, that the Sanarelli organism was in reality
a strain of the hog cholera bacillus and was in no way
connected with the etiology of yellow fever.[4] I cannot be sure what his principal mission in Cuba was
at that time. He remained in Havana for several days.
One afternoon he brought his son, Sergeant Walter
Lawrence Reed, to see me. Lawrence was at that
time stationed in Havana with the Coast Artillery.
He was a fine, husky young man who had enlisted
soon after the outbreak of the war and was working
for a commission. From 1935 to 1939 he was Inspector
General of the Army with the rank of Major General.
Since our first meeting in Havana, we have both enjoyed being stationed together in various places.

In May 1899 I received an order to report for duty
to Captain A. N. Stark, M. C., who was in command
of the hospital ship *Terry*. Stark, who was on the examining board which admitted me to the Service, had
asked for me. I was not keen about the change for I
was happy and content with my station at La Punta.
The *Terry* was used to bring sick from various Cuban
ports to Havana for transshipment to the United

[4] Reed and Carroll: Bacillus Icteroides and Bacillus Cholerae
Suis—A Preliminary Note. *Medical News*, April 29, 1899.

States. She was not then in Havana harbor and before she arrived, my order was revoked, as it had been decided that the ship would be discontinued as a hospital ship. The hospital ship *Missouri* plied between Havana and the States, bringing medical supplies and evacuating serious medical cases to United States ports. Major W. H. Arthur, M. C., was in command. He had also been a member of my examining board. These contacts with senior officers of my corps were pleasant features of my station in Havana.

About the middle of July, I had another visit from Walter Reed. On this visit or the one mentioned previously (May) he was investigating a reported epidemic of malaria in the Eighth United States Cavalry at Puerto Principe. He found that the disease was typhoid fever and not malaria. He was not making a formal inspection of conditions in Havana but wanted to check the situation to see what was going on. Besides, he was showing a kindly interest in my welfare. He went over my hospital records most carefully.

We had had some chronic recurrent cases of malaria whose original infection was contracted elsewhere, principally at Santiago in the spring of 1898. Furthermore, we had the reports of the blood findings and a treatment list to show him. Typhoid fever constituted our big problem, but he informed me that we had much less typhoid in our command than organizations in many other parts of Cuba. This was no doubt due to the better conditions in Havana, i.e., a good city water supply, sewers, and fewer flies. Typhoid "carriers," and recruits coming from infected camps in the States, no doubt accounted for most of our cases after we were free of the cases contracted in our unsanitary camp at Huntsville. Major Reed was keenly interested in our method of isolating suspicious cases of yellow fever and in the prompt assistance given me by the experts in that disease. It was always an event of importance to have a visit from Major Reed whose sterling qualities, soldierly bearing, and outstanding fitness in his specialty impressed me so greatly.

During April, May, and June, suspicious cases were quite frequently admitted to the hospital. Major Gorgas and his friends were alert, for the number of yellow fever cases in Havana had steadily increased, and by the end of July 1899, things began to be alarming. Our regiment had had no cases. The Second Coast Artillery at Cabaña Barracks was not so fortunate.[5] They were quartered in the old Spanish barracks of the fort and during July and August one officer and twenty-two men developed the disease, with seven deaths. This command was then moved out of the barracks and placed in tents outside of the fort. The epidemic ended at once.

[5] Annual Report of General Fitzhugh Lee, Department of Western Cuba, August 23, 1900, page 10.

FIG. 7. The Eighth Infantry at drill on the street in front of La Punta. A corner of the large Havana Carcel (prison) is shown.

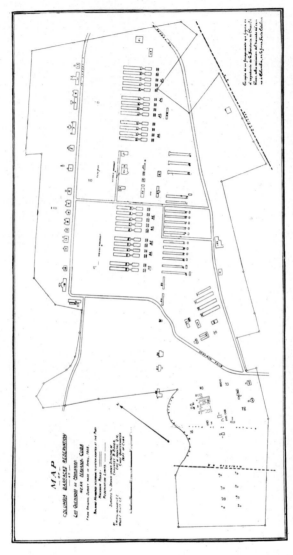

FIG. 8. Map of the Columbia Barracks reservation, 1902. The hospital area is at the left.

CHAPTER FOUR

YELLOW FEVER AT
LA PUNTA

EARLY in August 1899, our first case of yellow fever at La Punta developed. It was a frank case, the diagnosis was promptly made and the patient was transferred to Military Hospital No. 1. Major Fitzhugh Carter, M. C., was in command of that hospital and First Lieutenant Carl R. Darnall, M. C., was Executive Officer. Roger Post Ames, a contract surgeon, was on duty at the hospital and in charge of the yellow fever wards.

With the development of cases in other commands in the city and at Cabaña Barracks, and the alarming increase throughout the city, the authorities decided to move the troops away. At that time, there was no military necessity for keeping troops within the city limits. General Wood and his staff remained but the two regiments of Regulars were ordered away. The Eighth Infantry went to Columbia Barracks. The First and Third Battalions left Havana about July 20.

On August 12, Regimental Headquarters, Band, and the companies at La Punta marched via Vedado to a camp site about one mile east of the post and went into a quarantine camp for five days. On August 17, no case of yellow fever having developed, the command moved into the new field-type quarters and barracks which had recently been constructed at Camp Columbia. While the Seventh Army Corps had occupied this site from December 1898 until the late spring of 1899, it was known as Camp Columbia and this title clung to the place for years although the official title was changed at about this time to Columbia Barracks.

The post was located on a plateau, sloping gradually to the Gulf of Mexico about a mile to the north, thus providing excellent drainage. There were a few trees in scattered places but little or no shrubbery. Except in the heat of the day, it was comfortable, and the nights were delightful. In fact, it was a beautiful, healthful site for troops. While everyone had enjoyed the novelty of service in Havana, this was a most welcome change. For the first time since the regiment left its home station in the early spring of 1898 for war service, the command was comfortably sheltered. The Seventh United States Cavalry and two batteries of Field Artillery were already installed in the new quarters and barracks. In addition, there were several pack trains and wagon trains. Colonel T. A. Baldwin, Seventh Cavalry, the senior officer present, was in command.

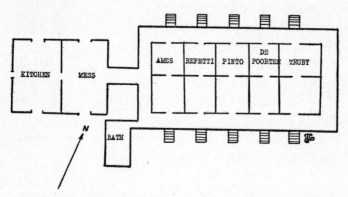

Fig. 9. Plan of medical officers' quarters (building No. 108). Columbia Barracks, December 1899.

The post extended southwestward for about three quarters of a mile from Buena Vista where the Eighth Infantry had camped in December 1898. The main highway from Havana to Quemados (Calzada Real) ran approximately parallel to the long axis of the military reservation and about a quarter of a mile away. The post hospital was at the extreme southwestern end of the post and entirely by itself—about one fourth of a mile from the nearest buildings of the main post. Residences on the outskirts of Quemados, however, came to within two hundred yards of our medical officers' quarters. General Lee Street, where yellow fever first appeared in the Quemados epidemic of 1900, ran from the Calzada Real to the corner of the hospital area.

Orders were promptly issued detaching me from the Eighth Infantry and assigning me to duty at the post hospital. Major S. P. Kramer, U. S. V., was in command of the hospital. Upon reporting, I was made Executive Officer of the hospital and also assigned to duty in the surgical ward. The surgical work was extensive because of the numerous accidents from the Cavalry, Field Artillery, and the large corral with its hundreds of mules.

The medical staff in August 1899 was as follows:

Major Solomon P. Kramer, U. S. Volunteers, Post Surgeon

First Lieutenant Albert E. Truby, U. S. A., Executive Officer; Ward Surgeon

Contract Surgeon Alvah S. Pinto, Ward Surgeon

Contract Surgeon John J. Repetti, Ward Surgeon and Medical Supply Officer

Contract Surgeon Lieven de Poorter, Jr., Post Sanitary Officer

Contract Surgeon Najeb M. Saleeby, Attending Surgeon.

Contract Surgeons John Gilbert and Clark I. Wertenbaker were present for a short time.

Dr. Saleeby lived in the main post and it was his duty to take sick call for the command and to attend to all emergencies. Our hospital received his patients whenever they required hospitalization. He was instructed to transfer all patients running a temperature at once, without any attempt to make a diagnosis. This plan worked perfectly and the command was protected by promptly removing contagious cases to our well-isolated hospital. Saleeby was a very good doctor and did his work faithfully.

Dr. Pinto was an excellent physician. It was almost uncanny the way he could promptly spot the perforation of a typhoid ulcer. In a letter (September 1941) from Dr. Pinto, now the Health Commissioner of Omaha, Nebraska, he says:

In the case of Nat. Field, Private, Eighth Infantry, we operated on a perforated typhoid ulcer. I had a "heck" of a time making the rest of you fellows believe it was a perforation, and no doubt you will remember it was 2:30 in the morning when we operated. This was the first operation for perforation of a typhoid ulcer ever attempted in the U. S. Army, and he recovered. The others we operated on subsequently were unsuccessful.

Dr. Pinto is probably right about the last statement but I have a feeling that we saved two out of about four cases by prompt surgical repair. The old sick and wounded reports would tell. Pinto had had an extensive experience in the treatment of that disease. We all considered him as the "star" diagnostician of the group. With his cheerful disposition and friendly attitude, he was popular with his confrères as well as with his patients. He came to Cuba with the Second Division Hospital.

Dr. Repetti was a humorous and congenial associate and also a fine doctor. He had also had service with the Second Division Hospital and elected to remain at Camp Columbia after that organization returned to the States. He had charge of our medical warehouse.

Dr. de Poorter was the post sanitary officer. This was a very important as well as a very difficult position to fill. Without a sewerage system and with wretched bathing facilities, the sanitary conditions were giving the medical authorities much concern. Typhoid fever was on the increase and was actually epidemic. The Quartermaster Department in Havana was not co-operating and recommendations of the sanitary experts were often ignored. "Reed troughs" with "odorless excavators" were, however, placed in operation about this time, with a marked reduction in the sick rate. Dr. de Poorter was active, efficient and tactful. His stories of experiences with the "odorless excavators" which we dubbed his "heavy artillery" gave us much amusement. With the installation of the sewerage system in the fall of 1899, his work was greatly lessened.

All of the medical officers were fully occupied with their duties. There were many cases of typhoid fever in the hospital. Each one did a day's work every day and spent many a night, too, in meeting emergencies which were constantly arising. All were young men about thirty years of age, serious in their work, and full of energy. It was most pleasing to me to get back to duty with a group of medical men of my own age and to take part in real hospital work again.

The hospital corps detachment consisted of from forty to seventy men with about seven noncommissioned officers (hospital stewards and acting hospital stewards). This group of men was as loyal and efficient as any I have ever known during my long service in the Medical Department. Their service in various camp hospitals had thoroughly fitted them for the duties at our hospital. Their heroism was shown in their daily work with typhoid fever and more especially when volunteers were needed to test the mosquito theory concerning yellow fever.

From four to eight women nurses, under contract, were also on duty at the hospital. We should have had many more. They were most faithful and efficient, worked regardless of hours and repeatedly demonstrated their importance to the army *under field conditions.*

The hospital grounds, located on this beautiful site 150 feet above sea level, were extensive and ideal for our needs. There was ample room for expansion in emergencies such as we experienced later in a dengue epidemic. The contour map shows the perfect natural drainage of the area, including that of the isolation camp. The few temporary buildings provided were widely scattered, the main group alone utilizing at least three acres of space between the 140 and 150 contour intervals. The 150 foot mark, the highest point in the area, was a few feet south of the officers' quarters. This magnificent site had formerly been occupied by the Second Division Hospital of the Seventh Army Corps. That command was returned to the United States in the spring (1899) and left us the temporary buildings mentioned. They were long, narrow, cheap wooden shacks used for barracks and the storage of medical supplies. Among them were several smaller buildings, one of which (Fig. 10, *89*) was used as an operating room. One small set of quarters (*106*) was also left by the Division Hospital. It was occupied by Dr. Lazear at the time he was taken sick in September 1900. In July (1899) a new building (*108*) had been constructed for bachelor medical officers. It provided five sets of quarters, each with two

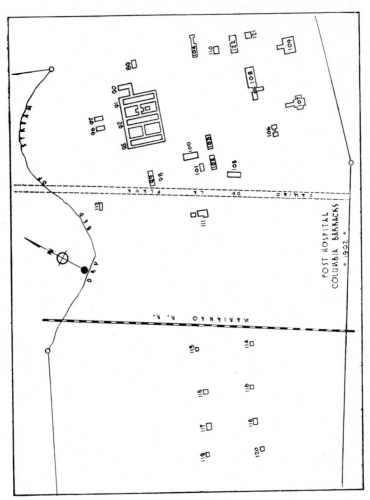

Fig. 10. Map of the hospital grounds, Columbia Barracks, 1902.

Key to Buildings Shown on Map in Figure 10

89. Reed's laboratory (original operating room)
90. Operating room
91.
92. } Wards
93.
96. Patient's mess room
97. Kitchen
98. Night men, quarters
99. Noncommissioned officer's quarters
100. Detachment mess
101. Lavatory
102.
103. } Hospital corps barracks
104. Original venereal ward
105. Warehouse
106. Dr. Lazear's quarters

107. Capt. Stark's quarters
108. Bachelors' quarters
109. Built in 1901 for Stark
110. Nurses' quarters
111. Disinfecting plant and Lambert's quarters
112. Morgue
113. Storage
114. Dr. Ames' office
115.
116. } Two-bed huts
117.
118. } Five-bed huts
119.
120. } Kitchens
121. Shelter for horses
122. Site of original receiving ward

Note: Nos. 121 and 122 did not appear on the 1902 map. They have been added here to show their approximate location before removal in 1900.

rooms about ten feet square. A wide porch extended
around the entire building, a mess building connected
with the southwest end and a bathroom with an im-
provised shower arrangement extended off one end of
the porch. This building, in addition to providing living accommodations, served as an office for each officer. It was therefore the real center of all our activities. The small office in the hospital served mainly as
a place for the clerks and their records. The doors
and windows of our quarters were open night and day
except during very severe storms. The resulting close
association of the officers was pleasant since everyone
co-operated and all were interesting and agreeable fellows. A fine mess, with an excellent cook, added to
the general contentment.

Our daily routine was regulated by the bugle calls
at post headquarters, the hospital musician repeating
the calls that applied to our activities. Everyone was
up early, the morning hours being the best of the
day. Breakfast at our mess was at 7 o'clock and at
8 o'clock the wards were ready for the doctors.
Lunch was at 12 noon and after about a half hour
of "bunk fatigue," we were back at work. There was
not much time for daytime sports, but in the late
afternoon we often went to La Playa, about a mile
away, for a swim in the surf of the Gulf. Occasionally,
I was turned out mounted by the Commanding Of-

ficer for parades and reviews since I was a member of his staff. In order to exercise my horse, I rode him on inspection work which took me to all parts of the large reservation and there were occasional rides with friends, especially of the Eighth Infantry.

After the day's work, a shower and a fresh white uniform added to our comfort and appearance. When dinner was announced, the hungry group was ready for the occasion which, by general desire, was carefree and happy but always with more formality than at other times.

The spacious porch around the building afforded a splendid meeting place during the delightful evening hours. Visitors called, we played games and in general had most pleasant times on that porch.

All of the sick during 1899 were cared for in tent wards on the flat area northward of the medical officers' quarters. These wards were made up of four hospital tents and a fly, providing space for sixteen patients. In the usual arrangement, two tents pitched end to end were separated from the next two by a tent fly which served as a central utility room. Each tent was also covered by a fly to provide space for air circulation. This added much to the comfort of the patients in the heat of the day. With the tent walls rolled up and ends open, the patients were fairly comfortable and our typhoid fever cases did exceedingly well in those tent wards as will be seen by our low mortality rate. Typhoid fever and surgical cases predominated. New and very well planned and constructed hospital buildings with all accessories including kitchen, mess and operating facilities were constructed and occupied early in 1900 (Fig. 10, *90–97*).

A railroad cut about ten feet deep passed through the southwestern part of the hospital grounds. It was a one track line running between Quemados and La Playa, a small fishing village on the shores of the Gulf. The grounds on the far side of the cut were barren with no habitations nearby. It was therefore an ideal site for an isolation camp. The Second Division Hospital had used it for that purpose and had left a few small, wooden shacks (Fig. 10, *115–120*) which were built for yellow fever but actually used for smallpox cases (Pinto). Therefore as they were not in good repair, we preferred to use tents for the few fever cases requiring isolation. One case of yellow fever was isolated and treated there in July 1899. During the epidemic of yellow fever at Quemados in 1900, the shacks were repaired and the isolation camp became the Columbia Barracks yellow fever hospital. The small buildings were then referred to by many as the yellow fever "wards." Dr. Ames had charge under the direction of the post surgeon. Major Kean,

Dr. Carroll, Dr. Lazear, and Private Dean were a few of the patients treated there. Dr. Lazear died there. The two buildings, *117* and *118*, were 10 by 16 feet and each provided accommodations for from three to five patients. The smaller buildings, *115* and *116*, were 7 by 9 feet in size and provided for one or two beds. Number *114* was still smaller and was used by Dr. Ames as an office. The other small buildings shown on the map were for storage and kitchens. Much of the information regarding the yellow fever hospital was given me by Gustav E. Lambert, who served at the hospital under Dr. Ames. It has been confirmed by Dr. Pinto and it all conforms to my recollections.

A short distance northwest of the isolation camp, we had the detention camp for the observation of all men who had been absent without leave (A.W.O.L.) from Columbia Barracks. They were isolated and kept under our close scrutiny from five to six days. Their clothing was taken away and disinfected and they were provided with the following: nightshirt, hat or helmet, and a pair of slippers. (The Seventh Cavalry wore campaign hats and the Infantry wore white helmets.) In this raiment they could not expect to get far away. However, the post commander provided an armed guard for this camp. When the yellow fever hospital became active (1900), the detention camp was moved elsewhere.

Our hospital was in real need of a receiving ward at the time of my arrival. A long temporary building (Fig. 10, *122*) near the medical officers' quarters was available for the purpose and we had it screened with wire netting of a fine mesh. All patients running a temperature were admitted there until a diagnosis was made and then transferred to the proper ward. I was the ward surgeon and when yellow fever was suspected, the patient was promptly transferred to the isolation camp.

Because of the primitive and very inadequate bathing facilities at the post, most patients admitted to the receiving ward required a hot bath. The bathing facilities at the hospital were also very crude. We had portable bath tubs for our typhoid fever cases and a few showers but no way of heating water for hot baths. It seemed to me that we could provide enough for the receiving ward in the daytime by simply laying a long line of pipe on the top of the ground. There was, I knew, plenty of iron pipe available but from past experience I anticipated trouble in obtaining any of it. My short service in the Army had, however, already taught me one thing, *viz.*, that commanding officers, quartermasters, and everyone else would do anything possible for a doctor if he explained that his requirements were necessary for

Fig. 11. The Second Division Hospital of the 7th Army Corps, commanded by Major Ira C. Brown, Surgeon, U.S.V. The small wooden building with the ventilator on the roof, and the white trimmings on door and windows was the operating room. It later became Walter Reed's laboratory (building No. 89). The method of joining the tents illustrates how they were arranged to provide the wards described in the text. (Army Medical Museum Neg. No. 67355.)

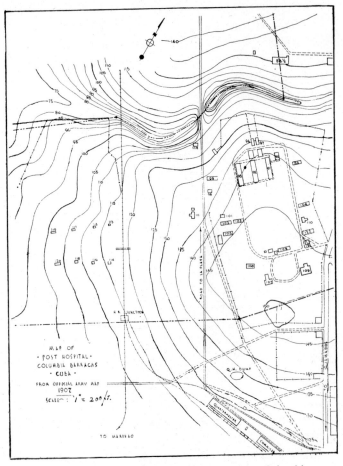

FIG. 12. Contour map of hospital grounds at Columbia
Barracks, 1907.

the treatment or comforts of sick men. Captain Goodale, the Quartermaster, was friendly enough but we knew him as a "tightwad" when it came to issuing supplies which were intended for some other project. I explained my mission to him and while he was not very optimistic about its success, he promptly *loaned* us the pipe to test the idea, provided we would install it with our own men. Within twenty-four hours, men of the hospital detachment had it connected. The surface pipe was painted black and in the middle of the day, the water was too hot to use unless mixed with the water from the regular mains. This simple device was of great help to our overworked nurses and a source of much comfort for the sick. A similar contrivance was later installed for the nurses' quarters and for the medical officers' quarters. The Quartermaster did not reclaim his pipe until 1900 when the new wards which were provided with modern comforts, including an ample supply of hot water, were occupied. The old receiving ward was torn down at that time; I have indicated its old location on the 1902 map (Fig. 10, *122*).

In September (1899) admissions for malaria increased. At the same time, other fever cases (in which no parasites could be found) developed. They were soon recognized as dengue fever and within a couple of weeks it was a raging epidemic. Ambulance loads came over from Dr. Saleeby every morning, afternoon, and evening. As the new ward buildings were still under construction, many additional hospital tents had to be erected to meet the emergency. The disease was mild and most patients were returned to duty in five or six days. Our small laboratory was overwhelmed and the need for a full time specialist in bacteriology was evident. Fortunately no coincident yellow fever epidemic occurred. The doctors, nurses, and enlisted men of the hospital corps were badly overworked for three or four weeks. A severe tropical wind and rain storm came in October and the epidemic ended more suddenly than it started. The hospital personnel escaped this epidemic of dengue. Our grounds were well drained by nature and there were no watering troughs, or undrained areas around bathhouses, such as existed in the main post. In this connection, the rainfall for the fiscal year ending June 30, 1900, is interesting.[6]

1899						1900						
JULY	AUG.	SEPT.	OCT.	NOV.	DEC.	JAN.	FEB.	MCH.	APR.	MAY	JUNE	TOTAL
*3.87	0.34	2.97	5.82	3.66	1.14	2.24	3.39	3.53	.39	9.93	3.43	40.76

* Figures represent inches.

[6] Annual Report of General Fitzhugh Lee, Department of Western Cuba, August 23, 1900.

Mr. J. H. Andrus, who volunteered for blood inoculation tests in the yellow fever experiments, and whose name is on the Congressional "Roll of Honor," gave me the following extract from his records:

On September 12th, 1899 while on "monkey drill"—I was then a member of the Bat. F, 2nd Art.—I was kicked off the horse I was riding by the horse ahead of me. My broken knee-cap was "wired" at post hospital by Major Kramer, assisted by Lieutenant Truby and Acting Assistant Surgeon, A. S. Pinto.

This information has enabled me to fix the latter part of that month as the approximate time of Major Kramer's departure from Columbia Barracks. He was much interested in surgery and I was greatly indebted to him for the opportunities he gave me in that work. With his departure I became Post Surgeon.

The "Army of Occupation" in Cuba was always short of medical officers of the regular service, especially seniors, and this explains why junior officers occupied such important positions. After the Santiago campaign, the demand for experienced medical officers by the large army in the Philippines drew heavily on the small Army Medical Corps which consisted of only 192 commissioned officers; viz., 1 brigadier general (the Surgeon General), 6 colonels,

10 lieutenant colonels, 50 majors, 70 captains and 55 lieutenants.*

The report of General Wood on June 30, 1901, shows the following number of medical officers on duty on the island of Cuba:

U. S. Army	Volunteer Army	Contract Surgeons
Majors 4	Majors 2	Doctors 8
Captains 1	Captains 8	Dentists 1
Lieutenants . . . 5		

The post hospital was within easy walking distance of the headquarters of the Department of Havana Province and Pinar del Rio at Quemados. Brigadier General Fitzhugh Lee was in command and Major Jefferson R. Kean was the chief surgeon. Kean was active and kept constant contact with the hospital. When we needed advice, he gave it. When we needed help, he never failed us. After our dengue epidemic, I explained the need for a full time officer for the laboratory at Columbia Barracks, and he promptly took

* On January 1, 1941, the authorized strength of the Medical Department, Regular Army, was as follows:

Medical Corps	1424
Dental Corps	316
Veterinary Corps	126
Medical Administrative Corps	126
Total	1992

steps to have a bacteriologist assigned to our hospital. The Department Laboratory with Contract Surgeon Aristides Agramonte in charge was located at Military Hospital No. 1, too far away for the routine work required at Columbia Barracks. As no medical officer qualified for this work was available in Cuba, the request went on to the War Department. In February 1900, Dr. Jesse W. Lazear arrived for duty in the laboratory as the result of this correspondence.

The Chief Surgeon's report [7] for the fiscal year ending June 30, 1900 gives the mean strength of troops in the Department of Western Cuba as 3,009 and at Columbia Barracks as 1,716. The morbidity-mortality rates for Columbia Barracks are given in the accompanying table.

	ARMY (1898) PER 1000	COLUMBIA BARRACKS (1900) PER 1000
Admissions to sick report	2,146	3,212
Constantly non-effective	83	77
Discharges for disability in line of duty		2.33
Discharges not in line of duty . .		12.82
Total discharges, disability . . .	11.58	15.15
Deaths, disease		7.
Deaths, injury		2.9
Total death rate	27.55	9.9

[7] Annual Report of General Fitzhugh Lee, Department of Western Cuba, August 23, 1900.

The last volunteer organization of the Seventh Army Corps left for the United States to be mustered out of the Service on April 19, 1899. The weekly admission record of typhoid fever at Camp Columbia from that date are given in the accompanying table.[8] In the third edition of Osler's "Practice of Medicine"

TYPHOID FEVER CASES AT CAMP COLUMBIA
April 29 to July 29, 1899

For Week Ending	No. of Cases	Strength of Command	Organizations Present
April 29 . . .	1		7th U. S. Cavalry
May 6 . . .	8		Two batteries,
May 13 . . .	2	930	Second Field
May 20 . . .	14		Artillery
May 27 . . .	10		
June 3 . . .	6		
June 10 . . .	20	830	
June 17 . . .	9		
June 24 . . .	4		
July 1	3		7th Cavalry
July 10 . . .	16	1,500	*Two batteries, F. A.*
July 15 . . .	1		Eight Companies
July 22 . . .	4		8th U. S.
July 29 . . .	2		Infantry joined about July 27th

Total cases of typhoid . . 100
Deaths . . . . 5 (including one civilian)

[8] Annual Report of General Fitzhugh Lee, August 15, 1899, Chief Surgeon's Section.

the mortality rate from typhoid fever (1898) at the Johns Hopkins Hospital is given as 7.1 per cent.

From April through July a real epidemic of typhoid fever existed in the Seventh Cavalry and Second Field Artillery and the weekly sanitary reports from the medical officers of all organizations reported that fact and urged completion of the sewer. The Chief Surgeon had personally supplemented these reports by special sanitary reports on April 8 and June 1, recommending in most urgent terms the completion of the sewer project. His report states:

The history of sanitary matters at Columbia Barracks is worthy of record. Nine months ago the Secretary of War, being desirous to make it a model camp, directed, upon the advice of the Surgeon General that a sewer should be constructed to carry off the wastes, the latter officer being of the opinion that it is extremely difficult in permanent camps to prevent epidemics of typhoid fever without the use of sewers.

The Second Volunteer Engineers of the Seventh Army Corps, Colonel Willard Young, U. S. V., Commanding, had piped an ample supply of excellent water to Camp Columbia from the Vento water works in January 1899. This organization then started work on the sewerage system which was to discharge into the Gulf of Mexico west of La Playa. Eight-inch

wrought iron pipe was screwed together and laid
along the bed of the railroad leading to La Playa. By
April it was practically finished except for four expansion joints, which were in the quartermaster warehouse in Havana, and reinforcing the supports in
places where the pipe had sagged. Colonel Young and
his command had been ordered home with the Seventh
Army Corps and the sewer project on April 15 was
turned over to the Quartermaster, Division of Cuba,
for completion. In the meantime the sewer line had
been inspected by a supposedly qualified civilian em-
ployee of the Chief Quartermaster's office. His report
led the Chief Quartermaster to conclude that "there
was no sewer—that only an alleged line of sewer
existed." So, in his action on the matter, the Chief
Quartermaster stated that "this office scarcely con-
templates recommending completion of the line of
pipe which, though never in use, now requires repair."

Thus, [as Kean says] the unsupported statement of one
man appears to have been sufficient for the abandonment
of the sewer which had cost three (3) months of labor
and tens of thousands of dollars.

Major Ira C. Brown, Surgeon, U. S. V., commanding the Second Division Hospital, had submitted his
sanitary report on March 1. Among other recom-

mendations was one which urged that the sewer be connected at the hospital. The nineteenth indorsement by the Chief Quartermaster, Division of Cuba, with his action as expressed above, reached Department Headquarters at Quemados (Kean's office) on June 7 and then things really began to hum. General Lee took an active part and Colonel O'Reilly, Chief Surgeon in Havana, did likewise, resulting in the prompt appointment by General Brooke's headquarters of a board of officers, headed by Colonel William M. Black, Chief Engineer, Division of Cuba, to investigate and report. By June 15, this board reported that the sewer could be placed in operation for $2,000 or less. On June 29 the work was placed in charge of Captain George L. Goodale, U. S. V., the camp quartermaster. The expansion joints were obtained and other necessary work was soon finished with his small force. The upper end of the sewer was connected to the hospital in September, to test its questioned efficiency. It worked perfectly and before the end of the year the "Reed troughs" (part of the odorless excavator system installed July 1) throughout the post were connected. New bathhouses were promptly constructed and all waste water piped to the sewer. Drainage of corrals and other wet places was taken care of and the improved morale of everyone, as well as the greatly reduced sick rate, was evidence enough of the importance of a sewerage system in a large permanent camp in the tropics. Looking backward, it is now plain to me that the epidemic of dengue at the post in the fall of 1899 was definitely due to the standing water around bathhouses and corrals where the mosquitoes responsible for transmitting the disease were bred. This sewer controversy is a splendid example of the difficulties experienced by the Medical Department in that period and exemplifies also the importance of heeding expert sanitary advice. One staff department of the Army will probably never again be able to block sanitary reports as happened in this case.

Shortly after July 1, 1899, there was a remarkable drop in the admission rate for diarrheal diseases. On the date mentioned, the odorless excavator system for disposal of excreta, recommended by the Typhoid Board (Walter Reed, Vaughan, and Shakespeare), was installed (G. O. 170, A. G. O. 1899). The admission rate per thousand in October 1899 was 200, and in February 1900 it was but 50. The rate for typhoid fever was 42 per thousand in July 1899 and by October it had dropped to 10. From February to June 1900, the rate was about 3 per thousand. During the latter period, the sewerage system was in operation and bathing facilities much improved.

Major General Leonard Wood, U. S. V., succeeded

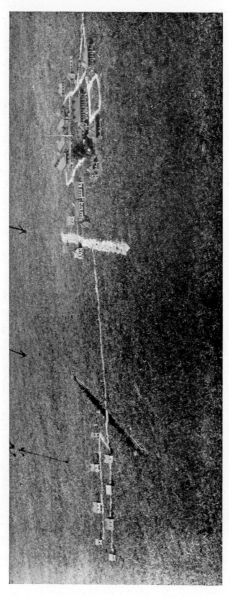

Fig. 13. The Idelfonso model, set up at Carlisle Barracks, Pennsylvania, according to scale. (Carlisle Barracks, photograph No. Q 334.)

FIG. 14. The detention camp (1899) for men who had been absent without leave. The guards, wearing white helmets, were from the 8th Infantry. The 7th Cavalry wore campaign hats. (Photograph by a member of the detachment.)

General Brooke as Governor General on December
20, 1899. A large reception was held for him at the
palace in Havana. Officers of the post, with Colonel
Randall leading, attended. (Colonel Baldwin was in
the United States on leave.) Wood's promotion was
not popular in the Army since he was a young officer
and did not belong to the "line" of the Army. He
was a captain in the Medical Corps of the Regular
Establishment but when he became a Major General
of Volunteers, he ranked all other officers in Cuba.
As the line passed the receiving party, there was evidence of a constrained attitude among the senior officers. As I came along, General Wood smiled and
said, "Young man, you're refreshing. I'm glad to see
you."

After much controversy about the Wood appointment, public opinion in time became almost universal
that he was the ideal man for the position because of
his medical background as well as his executive ability.
After all, the gravest problem which faced our Government in Cuba when it took over on January 1,
1899, was the maintenance of the health of the command under conditions which for centuries had been
frightful and the secret of which had not been unfolded. All other problems in Cuba were minor in
comparison. It was indeed a great medical problem
which faced General Wood. It gave him much anx-

iety. However, he proved to be the right man in the right place for he saw the possibility of solving the enigma of yellow fever.

When Reed arrived in June 1900 and the question of experimenting on human subjects came up in order to test the mosquito theory, Wood promptly approved the idea of using volunteers. I doubt if an older and more conservative Governor General, without a medical background, would have assumed such responsibility.

Cushing, in discussing the hearings by a Senate Committee (1900) on the Antivivisection Bill and the testimony of Professors Welch and Osler, had this to say about the discovery that the mosquito was responsible for the transmission of yellow fever: [9]

Had the discovery not been made, had one of the soldier-volunteers who contracted the disease (rather than the lamented Lazear, one of the Commission) died as a result of the experimental inoculations, one can imagine what a howl would have been raised on the floor of the Senate. . . . Had there not been an intelligent, courageous military Governor in Havana willing to take the responsibility for the carrying out of these experiments, without getting the permission of Congress—well, the Panama Canal would have been an impossibility.

[9] The Life of Sir William Osler. Vol. 1, p. 523.

In due time the Havana papers heard of the board's work and promptly attacked both Wood and Reed for experimenting on human subjects. Even in the discussion which followed the reading of the "Additional Note," which was the official report of the work at Camp Lazear, one of the doctors criticized the methods employed and objected to the use of human beings in such experiments.[10]

In October Captain Stark was ordered to duty at the hospital. He reported, but on November 1 went to the States on leave and toward the close of the year returned with his family. I welcomed his return, as the administrative duties of Surgeon of this large camp prevented my doing the amount of professional work which I wanted. I had become quite well acquainted with Stark in Havana and looked forward with much pleasure to serving under him. He was a brilliant young officer, always congenial and full of wit and humor. He particularly wanted to do surgery and here he had the opportunity he had been seeking. This service grew with his energy and enthusiasm so that it gave us all plenty of experience.

As the officers of the post now had comfortable quarters, and health conditions were greatly improved,

[10] Walter Reed: Baltimore address, April 1901. Senate Document No. 822, 61st Congress, 1911, p. 87.

their families began to arrive from the States. This en-
livened the garrison. Band concerts, parades, dances,
and all the other activities of a large Army post were
soon in full swing. A large open pavilion had been
erected near post headquarters where the dances were
held. Musicians from the two bands at the post furnished the music. Stark's family arrived and lived in
hospital tents, near our quarters (Fig. 10, *108*).

The evolution of the Stark quarters is interesting
and amusing. At first the Starks had a floored and
framed hospital tent. Then two additional tents were
placed on each side of the original tent for sleeping
quarters and one behind as a kitchen. Finally wooden
walls, roofs and porches were added and the little
house (Fig. 10, *107*) was the result. Lazear's quarters
were probably evolved in the same manner but that
was built before my arrival at the hospital. Major Ira
C. Brown, U. S. V., commanding the Second Division
Hospital, occupied the quarters (Pinto).

During the year 1899, typhoid fever, which had
been epidemic, was practically eliminated at the post.
There was a sudden and short epidemic of dengue
fever but fortunately yellow fever was not threaten-
ing us at the same time. The hospital was functioning
nicely and everyone seemed happy and contented
even though our living conditions were still somewhat
crude. The completion of the sewerage system and

the improved bathing facilities reduced the sick rate and brought us comforts we should have had at least six months before. I realized that I was getting fine professional experience and the idea of remaining in the Service grew stronger, but I was still undecided.

CHAPTER FIVE

"A YELLOW FEVER YEAR"–1900

IN the early months of the year, the climate of
Cuba is ideal. With our beautiful and healthful
location, we seemed to be most fortunately situated.
Everything was peaceful. General Lee, in his report, stated:

If vigilance is at all times exercised, troops can be kept
in the tropics without loss of health, vigor or military efficiency, but we must never forget that the germs of yellow fever are ever present and are still a mystery to the
medical profession. Apparently they lie dormant in many
localities for several years and then from inexplicable
reasons recommence their destructive work.

Continuing, he said:

Quemados and Marianao are pretty towns situated some
eight miles from Havana on a high elevated plateau
overlooking the ocean. They are health resorts and during the Summer are filled with people from Havana
escaping from the heat and dangers of disease.

No one thought that we were in danger of an epidemic at Quemados or at Camp Columbia. However, the Cubans called it a "yellow fever year," probably because no epidemic had occurred the year before.

In February 1900 Dr. Jesse W. Lazear came from Baltimore under War Department orders. He was a bacteriologist, selected by the Surgeon General's office for duty in our laboratory, as the result of our report of the urgent need for someone to fill that position. He was a contract surgeon. There was much work to be done. Lazear did it promptly and efficiently. He also had time for research work with especial reference to yellow fever, and he utilized it fully. Lazear soon became one of the most respected and efficient members of our staff. He was always courteous and agreeable and went about his work in our laboratory with enthusiasm. Every member of the staff was fond of him. Mrs. Lazear was with him and they had the small set of married officers' quarters southwest of the bachelor medical officers' quarters. They took their meals at our mess.

My sister came from New York to pay me a visit and she occupied my quarters while I "bunked" with one of my confrères. This gave us two ladies in the mess and resulted in a little more decorum and formality, especially at meal times. However, we had grand times. During March we made numerous sightseeing trips to Havana and other points of interest. One of these was a visit to Morro Castle and Cabaña Fortress. In the party were Dr. and Mrs. Lazear, Dr. Repetti, Dr. de Poorter, my sister and myself. Untold numbers of Cubans had been reportedly "butchered" against the massive walls of the moats of the Fortress.

In April, Mrs. Lazear, my sister, and Dr. Repetti sailed for New York on the transport *Sedgwick*. Dr. Repetti had decided to return to his home in Washington, D. C., and enter private practice.

Dr. Roger Post Ames (a contract surgeon) reported for duty at our hospital on April 10, 1900. He had been on duty at Military Hospital No. 1 in Havana. He brought with him an excellent record as a yellow fever expert.

On May 1, the officer personnel of the hospital consisted of the following: Stark, Truby, Pinto, de Poorter, Ames, and Lazear, in order of rank. Acting assistant surgeons (contract surgeons) took rank in accordance with the date of their contracts with the Government. A short time later, Contract Surgeons Raoul Amador, son of a former President of the Republic of Panama, and Robert P. Cooke reported for duty.

In March and April 1900, Major Walter Reed was in Havana investigating at this time the use of electro-zone as a germicide. Colonel William Black had for some time been manufacturing the liquid from sea water. During 1899 and 1900, large tank wagons of the street sprinkling type hauled it about and wet down the city streets. Reed found that electrozone was more expensive and less efficient for this purpose than a solution made with ordinary chloride of lime, the latter having more free chlorine than electrozone had.

During this trip to Havana (March and April), Walter Reed lived with us for some time at the bachelor medical officers' quarters at Columbia Barracks. We had plenty of room and it was a great privilege to have him with us. He found our quarters more comfortable and agreeable than hotels in Havana. Our mess at that time was excellent and all of its members were active and interesting young doctors. We were of course on our best behavior but he was jovial and soon put us at ease. He knew how to join in with young doctors and share in their jokes and amusements. Whenever possible, he sought for whatever information we could give him on our experiences in the southern camps and in Cuba. He became interested in Dr. Lazear and spent considerable time with him at the laboratory. In the evening, our delightful porch was a general meeting place and many of Walter Reed's friends came to call. I know that this gave him great pleasure. Yellow fever, the subject which he had been studying for

some time, was constantly on his mind and he was untiring in discussing it with all of the visiting physicians.
Dr. Finlay's theory of mosquito transmission was often
discussed and the fact that malaria was known to be
a mosquito-borne disease made Finlay's theory more
plausible.

It is my belief that when Reed left us for the States
in April, he had fully decided to ask General Sternberg to send him back to Cuba to continue his studies
of this disease. I know that he felt that this was the
time (1900) and the place (Columbia Barracks) for
intensive investigations on the etiology of yellow
fever. Upon reaching Washington he of course reported his observations on his mission to General
Sternberg and, at the same time, undoubtedly suggested that he be ordered to Columbia Barracks with
suitable personnel and equipment to continue his
work on yellow fever. General Sternberg, who himself had spent years in studying this disease and who
now was responsible for the health of the army in
Cuba, was naturally anxious to continue the fight.
The records show that on May 23 the Surgeon General requested orders of the War Department for
Major Reed and Contract Surgeon Carroll to report
to the Commanding Officer, Columbia Barracks, Cuba,
where with the addition of Drs. Agramonte and Lazear, a board would be formed "for the purpose of

Fig. 15. Hospital buildings, March 1900. New operating room at right is under construction. Lieutenant Truby approaching his quarters after drilling the detachment. The scene of the Cornwell painting (frontispiece), was at the steps which are just in front of him. The walk was made of white limestone rock from a nearby quarry.

FIG. 16. The old tree by Dr. Lazear's quarters. Alec and Tom Stark.

pursuing scientific investigation with reference to the infectious diseases prevalent on the island of Cuba and especially of yellow fever." [11] The War Department approved the recommendations and the orders were promptly issued. Reed and Carroll arrived at Columbia Barracks on June 25. The word *Commission* is often used instead of the Army term when speaking of the Reed *Board*.

On May 1, 1900, the Departments of Havana and Pinar del Rio were consolidated and the following order was issued:

HEADQUARTERS DEPARTMENT OF HAVANA AND PINAR DEL RIO

GENERAL ORDERS

NO.   I

QUEMADOS, CUBA, *May 1, 1900*

The undersigned hereby assumes command of the Department of Havana and Pinar del Rio, pursuant to General Orders No. 47, c. s. Headquarters of the Army, A. G. O., which consolidates, to take effect this date, the former Department of Havana and the Department of the Province of Havana and Pinar del Rio into one military department.

FITZHUGH LEE

Brigadier General, U. S. Volunteers

[11] George Miller Sternberg: A Biography. American Medical Association, 1920, p. 214.

Major Kean continued as Chief Surgeon and Major Gorgas was made Sanitary Officer of Havana succeeding Major Davis, U. S. V. (February 15, 1900).

On May 15, I was ordered to Guanajay Barracks, twenty miles west of Quemados. During the next few weeks, however, I was required to make several trips to Department Headquarters and Columbia Barracks. One of these, as a member of the examining board, kept me there for a week during which time I lived in my old quarters. These trips kept me in close touch with events.

The prediction that this was to be a "yellow fever year" was soon confirmed. The clean and beautiful village of Quemados on the border of the hospital grounds was one of the first places to be attacked. On May 19, yellow fever appeared at No. 20 General Lee Street, only a few hundred yards from the hospital. It spread rapidly to other houses on the same street and then to houses on the nearby intersecting street, Calzada Real. Most of the residents on these streets were non-immune Americans serving on General Lee's staff. Some were married civilian employees from Columbia Barracks who could not get quarters at the post.

From May 16 to June 30, there were thirty-two cases with eight deaths. Three of these cases developed in soldiers from Columbia Barracks who were work-

ing in the infected district. These three men were
treated in the post yellow fever hospital and all recovered. No secondary cases in the post resulted as
there were very few *A. aegypti* (*Culex fasciatus*) mosquitoes since we were provided at that time with a good
piped water supply and a new sewerage system which
removed waste water and provided good drainage.
During the next few weeks, eighteen additional cases
with four deaths resulted. Seven of these, with one
death, were among soldiers from Columbia Barracks.
The infection of these cases was again definitely traced
to Quemados where the soldiers worked; and again
no secondary cases resulted at the post, as all fever
cases were promptly isolated and treated in the hospital. Major Edmunds of General Lee's staff died. Major
J. R. Kean, our Chief Surgeon, recovered as did one
or two other officers who had quarters in the infected
zone.

The post hospital was called upon for nurses, both
men and women, to assist in the care of the Quemados
patients in their homes. Several of them contracted
the disease, one nurse and one man dying. Dr. Ames
also helped in the care of some of the patients who
were treated in their homes.

At this time, it was decided to repair the small
wooden shacks in the hospital isolation camp which
was described in the previous chapter. A foot bridge

was built over the railroad cut, as the activities increased. Sick soldiers and civilian employees from the Quemados epidemic were then brought there for treatment. Major Kean was admitted to hut No. 118 (Dr. Pinto's statement) on June 21 and was seen there by Walter Reed on June 25, the day of his arrival in Cuba. Later some of the cases from General Wood's staff and the three experimental cases (Carroll, "XY," and Lazear) were all treated there.

All of the experimental cases from Camp Lazear were likewise admitted and treated in these wards. None of them died. Ames saw to it that these men were placed under treatment upon the appearance of the first symptoms and then, even before a positive diagnosis could be made, had them transferred to these "wards."

Ames was one of the most capable of the doctors who were sent to Cuba under contract for this kind of service. He was usually right in his early diagnosis and had remarkable success in the treatment of yellow fever patients. He was convinced that yellow fever was not contagious and he was constantly playing practical jokes on members of our staff, all tending to drive away any fear that anyone may have had about the contagiousness of yellow fever. Ames was favorably inclined to the mosquito theory and became fully convinced by Lazear's results. Besides being a fine doctor, Ames was an interesting character. He possessed no desire, nor did he have the aptitude for military service. His age at that time was probably about thirty-five years.

A private of our Hospital Corps Detachment, G. E. Lambert, was dubbed by the men as "Ames' Man Friday." He was most loyal and faithful. Ames had this to say of him in a letter dated November 12, 1901:

During the epidemic at Quemados, near Columbia Barracks, Cuba, he was always my important right hand man. Nearly all cases of yellow fever (over 67), either natural or experimental, attended by me in part or whole, were nursed by this competent soldier. The general supervision of the yellow fever wards and the running of the large disinfecting plant was entrusted to his care.

He was in charge of most of the cases which later on came from Camp Lazear, but was not on the cases of Carroll, "XY," or Lazear. Lambert was a non-immune and he and other non-immune attendants at the yellow fever hospital escaped infection. There were no mosquitoes.

In Quemados, *A. aegypti* mosquitoes were always present. Cisterns and other large uncovered containers provided the principal water supply of the town, and these of course furnished ideal breeding places for *A. aegypti*. Many of the cases in this epidemic were treated in their homes. Consequently more and more mosquitoes became infected and found their way to other parts of the community. In Quemados, all bedding and clothing in infected homes were burned. Other household property, as well as the entire interior of the buildings, was thoroughly disinfected. However, the common domestic mosquito, *A. aegypti* remained unmolested as the Finlay theory had at that time practically no supporters in Cuba. Had this theory been favorably considered by prominent Cuban physicians, the United States Army would certainly have made an intensive campaign against *A. aegypti*.

The importance of Dr. Lazear's work in our laboratory at the time of the Quemados epidemic should be noted. The Department Chief Surgeon, in his report for June 30, 1900, had this to say of Lazear and his work:

Since February Columbia Barracks has had the great advantage of an expert bacteriologist, Act. Asst. Surgeon J. W. Lazear, to make routine blood examination in all fever cases and thus facilitate accurate, differential diagnoses.

The ability to thus promptly exclude malaria and typhoid has been of immense assistance to a prompt diagnosis in the recent outbreak of yellow fever. Where blood examinations of cases at other posts were desired, slides were sent by mail and his report sent by telegraph.

Dr. Lazear has found that during the first half of the calendar year the malaria-bearing mosquito (anopheles) is not prevalent at Columbia Barracks and the malarial attacks observed are entirely recurrences of old infections. After June the anopheles become abundant.[12]

During May and June he was taking full advantage of the opportunity of studying the nearby cases of yellow fever and in making blood cultures for study in his laboratory. Other duties were also added by such orders as the following:

HEADQUARTERS DEPARTMENT OF HAVANA AND PINAR DEL RIO

CIVIL ORDERS

NO.   5

QUEMADOS, CUBA, *May 31, 1900*

Upon the recommendation of the Chief Surgeon, in order to secure a prompt and accurate diagnosis in cases of suspected yellow fever incurring in this municipality, the following board of medical examiners is hereby appointed, the civilian members named having indicated their willingness to serve:

Dr. Nicacio Silverio, Marianao, Chairman;

Dr. Manuel Herrera, Sanitary Inspector;

Dr. Eduardo Angles, Municipal Physician;

Acting Assistant Surgeon Roger P. Ames, U. S. Army;

[12] Annual Report of General Fitzhugh Lee, August 23, 1900, Chief Surgeon's Section.

Acting Assistant Surgeon J. W. Lazear, U. S. Army, Recorder.

This Board will examine all suspicious cases as often as may be necessary to come to a finding, and make prompt report direct to the Chief Surgeon of the Department. It shall be the duty of members, as far as possible, to report upon the source of infection in each case. At least three members of the board will be present at each consultation, and any member not in the employ of the Government will receive compensation from the Government at the rate of three (3) dollars for each consultation, to be paid by the Disbursing Officer of the Department from the allotment for sanitary purpose.

The Ayuntamiento of Marianao will take the necessary action to require all physicians in the municipality to promptly report all cases of suspected yellow fever to a member of this board. Any member upon receiving such report will have authority to convene the board.

By command of Brigadier General Lee:

R. E. Michie
Assistant Adjutant General

On June 18 a camp was opened in Quemados with Major R. F. Echeverria, Surgeon, U. S. V., in charge, as a place of temporary residence for such non-immunes living in the infected district as the Chief Surgeon determined should be removed. "Finally all saloons and resorts in Quemados were closed and *all* non-immunes removed from Quemados into camp." [13]

This epidemic with fifty cases and twelve deaths in one of the finest and most sanitary villages in Cuba disturbed everyone and left a lasting impression.

[13] Annual Report of General Fitzhugh Lee, August 23, 1900.

CHAPTER SIX

THE REED BOARD BEGINS WORK

A S PREVIOUSLY stated, the Reed Board organized and began its work on June 25, 1900. Captain Stark provided quarters for Reed and Carroll in the
building (Fig. 10, *108*) used by bachelor medical officers on duty at the hospital. Reed occupied the second
set and Carroll the fourth set from the east end of the
building. These plain sets of quarters consisting of
two rooms, each about ten feet square, with a nearby
shower bath, and an excellent officers' mess, provided
all the comforts desired by Reed and Carroll.

Reed felt that it was most important that the Board
finish investigations on the Sanarelli theory.

At the time of our arrival in Cuba—June 1900—the
situation as regards the etiology of yellow fever may be
briefly stated as follows: The claims of all investigators
for the discovery of the specific agent of this disease had
been disproved by the exhaustive work of Sternberg,
published in 1890, except that made by Dr. Sanarelli, in
June 1897, for his bacillus icteroides. I need not take
up time here with mention of those who had investigated

FIG. 17. The hospital buildings at Columbia Barracks,
November 1900.

FIG. 18. Medical officers' quarters (building No. 108). X indicates
Major Reed's quarters; the arrow points toward Dr. Lazear's quarters; a signal corps telephone pole is prominent in the foreground.
(From official reports.)

Fig. 19. The "Surgery," Second Division Hospital. It was Walter Reed's laboratory in 1900. (Army Medical Museum, Neg. No. 67355.)

Sanarelli's claim, except to state that the confirmation
of his discovery came chiefly from workers in the
United States, of whom I may speak of Achinard and
Woodson, of New Orleans, and especially of Wasdin and
Geddings, of the Marine-Hospital Service. The latter,
in a report submitted during the summer of 1899, accepted in the fullest Sanarelli's claim for the specific
character of bacillus icteroides, basing their confirmation
on the finding of this bacillus in 13 out of 14 cases of
yellow fever studied by them in the city of Havana.
Under these circumstances, it was of the first importance
that we should give our entire time to the search for
bacillus icteroides in the bodies of yellow-fever cases.[14]

The nearby epidemic at Quemados and the cases
being treated in the yellow fever wards at Columbia
Barracks greatly facilitated the work of the board. I
quote a letter from Major Walter Reed to the Surgeon
General:

MY DEAR GENERAL STERNBERG: Your favor of the 22nd
inst. enclosing a letter from Dr. Vaughan has been received.
We arrived at this camp Monday afternoon, the 25th,
and were soon comfortably provided for by Dr. Stark.
We have already organized as a board and have begun
work. Yesterday we took careful cultures from two

[14] Walter Reed: Baltimore address, April 1901. Senate Document No. 822, 1911, p. 91.

cases that have slightly passed the most active stage. Lazear has cultures from three autopsies to be worked up. This afternoon we will take cultures from the blood of a case admitted to camp hospital last evening and will continue to take cultures each successive day. We can get material from another case at the detention camp. Upon my recommendation, Agramonte appears to have adopted wise measures here. Lazear and I will go probably to Cienfuegos next week to look into an epidemic of malarial fever amongst Second Infantry there. Our baggage (laboratory equipment) did not arrive on *Sedgwick*. Have asked General Humphrey to cable Q. M. General to have it forwarded by Ward Line of steamers. Please assist us at your end of the line.

Sincerely yours,
WALTER REED [15]

This letter was no doubt written on June 27. Blood culture work with especial reference to the Sanarelli organism had already started. The "wise measures" adopted by Agramonte probably referred to his studies and work on the same organism at the Department laboratory. I am quite certain that the proposed trip to Cienfuegos was never made.

While the continuation of their studies on *Bacillus icteroides* was important, there was time to begin pre-

[15] George Miller Sternberg: A Biography. American Medical Association, 1920, p. 220.

liminary studies on the other theories. Consequently the members of the Board made Dr. Finlay a visit soon after they organized late in June or early in July (Pinto) and brought back mosquito larvae and eggs. Lazear was at once placed in charge of this work as he had had more experience in entomology than the other members, and his selection for this duty was fortunate. Reed selected Carroll to pursue studies on the intestinal flora, a task which he was well qualified to perform. Agramonte remained at his full-time job at the Department laboratory (Military Hospital No. 1) in Havana. There was no one to replace him, and Reed never asked to have him relieved from those duties. He planned to use Agramonte for making autopsies and for pathological work if and when such work was required. There were, however, no deaths resulting from the experiments at Camp Lazear. Reed continued in general charge and supervised and assisted in all the work.

Inferences have been drawn that Reed was not interested in the mosquito theory at that time. Nothing could be further from the truth and furthermore he had been instructed by General Sternberg to study the insect theories. Sternberg says:

Having for years given thought to this subject, I became some time since impressed with the view that in yellow fever, as in malarial fevers, there is an "intermediate host." I therefore suggested to Dr. Reed, president of the board appointed upon my recommendation for the study of this disease to the Island of Cuba, that he should give special attention to the possibility of transmission by some insect, although the experiments of Finlay seemed to show that this insect was not a mosquito of the genus Culex, such as he had used in his inoculation experiments. I also urged that efforts should be made to ascertain definitely whether the disease can be communicated from man to man by blood inoculations.[16]

During one of my visits to Columbia Barracks about July 20, 1900, two British scientists, Drs. Durham and Myers, were discussing yellow fever with Major Reed. They were commissioned by the Liverpool School of Tropical Medicine to study the disease in South America and had decided to visit Havana en route to get any information that would be helpful to them. They reached Havana about July 18 and remained a week or ten days. Reed took them through his laboratory and freely outlined the Board's work including the plans for testing the mosquito theory. They saw the work then in progress, including the raising and caring for mosquitoes. On a large table in the center of the room there were several glass laboratory jars contain-

[16] George M. Sternberg: The Transmission of Yellow Fever by Mosquitoes. *Popular Science Monthly*, July 1901.

ing mosquitoes. There was a petri dish with a few drops of sweetened water and a piece of banana in each jar. Later it was found necessary to nourish the mosquitoes by letting the uninfected mosquitoes bite the hands of the laboratory personnel. Reed also told the visitors of Carter's findings in 1898 at Orwood and Taylor in Mississippi, which had really become Reed's guiding light in working out the mosquito theory. He states in the "Preliminary Note" that these foreign observers were duly impressed by Carter's observations. Is there any doubt that Reed was not impressed by the same findings?

When the Second Division Hospital personnel departed in the spring of 1899, they left a small wooden building (Fig. 10, *89*) which was used by them (and later by us) as an operating room. The dimensions of this building were approximately 16 by 24 feet. A new operating pavilion and new ward buildings were ready for occupancy early in 1900. The old operating building then became available for treating pus cases and for venereal work. When Reed came, it was converted into a laboratory for the use of the Board. It was in this building that Reed, Carroll, and Lazear did all of their work. The plan of the interior of this laboratory was given me by Mr. J. H. Andrus, who was on duty at the laboratory in 1900 under the direction of Major Reed.

One of the most faithful and important men who worked for this board was Hospital Steward John Neate. His name has rarely been mentioned in the

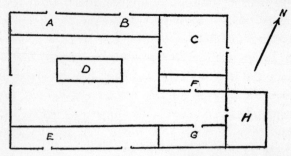

FIG. 20. Diagram of the Reed Board laboratory, Columbia Barracks, 1900. *A*, Major Reed's microscope on a long, high table in front of a large window providing a good north light. *B*, Dr. Carroll's microscope. *C*, Steward Neate's quarters. *D*, Table with large glass laboratory jars containing mosquitoes. *E*, Table with more jars, microtome, and other equipment. *F*, small room with incubator and shelves filled with hundreds of cultures in test tubes. *G*, Small room with shelves and table for supplies; two monkeys in cages were kept in this room, one of them died of pneumonia. *H*, Small addition for housing guinea pigs.

stories connected with these historical achievements. Reed had him ordered to Cuba from his Washington laboratory to fill the same position as the noncommissioned officer in charge of the Board's laboratory. Actually therefore he was a very important and integral part of the working force of that Board. He was competent to do all of the routine work in a bacteriological laboratory and Reed knew him to be reliable and efficient. He was also placed in full charge of raising and caring for Lazear's mosquitoes. This became very hazardous and exacting work, especially when it was found that mosquitoes could transmit yellow fever. Exciting times occurred when an infected mosquito escaped from her glass jar in the laboratory or in the small screened room at Camp Lazear where infected mosquitoes were kept during the work at that place. General Gorgas relates this humorous story of such an experience:

I once saw a party of twelve or fifteen doctors in the mosquito room one day when the mosquito-bar covering of the jar accidentally came off and the insects escaped into the room. These doctors had come from other countries to investigate the subject, and were not then convinced that the mosquito carried yellow fever. Still, they did not care to put the matter to a practical test in their own persons, and got out of the room so rapidly that the wire-screen door was broken down during their exit. It happened that the mosquitoes in this jar had never bitten a yellow-fever patient and were not infected.

No accidents with mosquitoes happened, however, thanks to the foresight of Reed and Lazear, and to Neate's efficiency. Major Reed depended greatly on Hospital Steward Neate and if he (Reed) had been alive when Congress made the awards to the heroes of this work, I feel sure that this man's name would

have been included. Dr. Neate died in Washington in
1912.*

General J. R. Kean, in reviewing the first rough
draft of this story, wrote me as follows:

I am much pleased to have you bring to light the work
of Sergeant Neate and I know it would please Walter
Reed if the spirits of the dead could follow the small
affairs of this world. I remember that he came to me
and spoke as you have done of Neate's faithful reliability
and said that he would like to get a gratuity for him.
(You know General Wood had put the fund in my
hands for disbursement.) So he proposed that Neate
should be the guinea pig for a test to see if the mosquito
Culex Pungens could carry yellow fever. It was done
and he got his $100. but it did not come within the
specifications for the Roll of Honor.

Coincident with the epidemic in Quemados, yellow
fever appeared in many places in Cuba: Havana, Vedado, Matanzas, Santa Clara, Cienfuegos, Santiago,
Guanajay, and Pinar del Rio. In the latter place, the
surgeon of the post lost eight patients from April 20
to July 16 from what he called "pernicious malaria."

---

* Hospital Steward Neate continued to serve at the laboratory
of the Army Medical School after Reed's death; first under
Carroll, then under Col. Frederick F. Russell. Neate graduated in
Medicine while still on duty in the laboratory. For several years
he was pathologist at the Woman's Hospital, Washington, D. C.

On July 17, Captain Stark, who was Acting Chief
Surgeon at that time (Major Kean was on leave recovering from his attack of yellow fever in June),
suspected that yellow fever was causing the deaths at
Pinar del Rio Barracks. He wired the post surgeon asking if yellow fever existed there. A negative reply was
received.[17] Acting Assistant Surgeon Agramonte was
then sent to inspect. He arrived on the 19th, in time to
hold an autopsy on the case of general prisoner A. H.
who died on the 18th. . . . "The typical lesions of yellow fever were found." Three patients in the hospital
at the time were likewise diagnosed as cases of yellow
fever. Also seven suspects were found sick in the
hospital. Agramonte was on this duty because of his
position in the Department laboratory and not because of his status as a member of the Reed Board.

After Agramonte reported his findings to the Chief
Surgeon, Reed decided to personally investigate. Agramonte was still there when Reed arrived on July 21;
". . . a body was sectioned that same afternoon. It
was yellow fever." Reed made a careful survey of the
situation and, with the mosquito theory in mind, made
some very important observations regarding a case
which had developed in the guardhouse among the
prisoners who had had no contact with the infected

[17] Annual Report of General Fitzhugh Lee, August 23, 1900,
Chief Surgeon's Section, p. 6.

town or sick people. If a mosquito could transmit the disease, the explanation would be simple for the iron bars on the open windows and the guard at the door did not keep out mosquitoes, although they did keep the men away from infected places.

Amid all the trying activities of this period at the hospital, the two lively Stark boys, Alec and Tom, about 4 and 3 years of age respectively, were having a grand time. One day they became thoroughly messed up by spilling the contents of a laboratory container which one of the doctors had left standing on the porch railing in front of his quarters. Walter Reed discovered the boys in this condition, and with a boy under each arm rushed them to the hospital where they were scrubbed up and disinfected. The liquid was a recent specimen of black vomit. Both boys have been officers in the United States Army for many years and both, at this writing, are colonels.

A medical examining board was convened in Havana in the summer of 1900 to examine contract surgeons who wanted to enter the regular service. M. A. W. Shockley, T. C. Lyster, and W. N. Bispham were the successful candidates, receiving their commissions in October 1900 as lieutenants in the Medical Corps.

At this time the number of departments in the Division of Cuba was reduced to two: the Eastern and Western departments.

HEADQUARTERS DEPARTMENT OF WESTERN CUBA

GENERAL ORDERS

NO.   I

QUEMADOS, CUBA, *July 24, 1900*

Pursuant to telegraphic instructions from the Adjutant General's Office, dated Washington, July 21st, the undersigned hereby assumes command of the Department of Western Cuba. This Department consists of the former Department of Matanzas and Santa Clara and the former Department of Havana and Pinar del Rio, comprising the Provinces of Santa Clara, Matanzas, Havana and Pinar del Rio.

Existing orders and circulars of the former Department of Matanzas and Santa Clara will continue in force for troops stationed in that department until further orders.

FITZHUGH LEE

Brigadier General, U. S. Volunteers

CHAPTER SEVEN

RAPIDLY CHANGING SCENES

L ET US go back to May 15, the date of my arrival at Guanajay, twenty miles west of Quemados, where I relieved Captain W. W. Quinton as Post Surgeon. The post was beautifully situated and was garrisoned by a battalion of the First United States Infantry. The hospital was at the entrance gate under very large, beautiful trees which furnished welcome shade during the heat of the day. The native village came right up to our fence. Mosquitoes were plentiful and they were nearly all *A. aegypti*. All of the post buildings were of American construction, similar to those at Columbia Barracks. Dr. John F. Dunshie, a contract surgeon, was my assistant. He was an immune and well qualified in the diagnosis and treatment of yellow fever.

Our detachment of the Hospital Corps consisted of an acting steward and about eight men. I was soon impressed with the training they had had and their bravery and faithfulness in nursing cases of yellow

fever. None of them was immune. Those whom I remember were:

Acting Hospital Steward Claude M. Cook
Private John E. Courtney
Private John H. Andrus
Private Frank M. Dawley
Private John D. Schwieger
Private Nels Rasmussen

The Commanding Officer of the post was a major of
Infantry.

Prior to my arrival, there had been considerable
yellow fever in the town and a few cases had developed in the command. In addition to my duties at the
post I found myself, by orders from Division Headquarters, Sanitary Officer of the town. It was well
policed and generally clean. The Alcalde and the
"medicos" were friendly and anxious to co-operate.
All yellow fever cases were promptly reported to me
and isolated. During June there was no epidemic but
sporadic cases appeared from time to time. In the
latter half of July, several of our soldiers developed
the disease, including Private Schwieger of the hospital
detachment who had been nursing our yellow fever
cases. About the same time the troops of our command
were ordered to return to the United States and I was
included in the order.

The post was to be abandoned. Dr. Dunshie and the

members of the Hospital Corps Detachment were to go to Columbia Barracks. In order that the troops could have a free bill of health on sailing day, August 2, we established a strict quarantine against the town and against our hospital. Dunshie ran the hospital and I moved to the bachelor building, took sick call and treated the men in their barracks. This was done about a week before sailing and not a single case developed during that time or on the voyage to New York. The troops left Guanajay by train early on August 2. In Havana we had a long, hot march to the docks. There all baggage was loaded on a lighter and taken to the quarantine station for disinfection. Lieutenant Grosvenor L. Townsend, First United States Infantry, and I were detailed by the Commanding Officer to go with it. Everything had to be passed through the enormous Marine Hospital autoclaves and it was late afternoon before we returned with the baggage to the transport dock. There we received the news that several of the officers were under arrest and that our sailing time had been postponed.

The troops had been comfortably sheltered from the sun on one of the large docks in charge of a few officers. The men were not allowed to leave the dock owing to the danger of contracting yellow fever in the infected city. The other officers of the battalion found a nearby cafe where they could obtain a fine lunch and be comfortable. They had all been through the trying Santiago campaign, the depressing pest-stricken camps in the South, and a year and a half of hard service in Cuba. Now they were on their way back to "God's country." Some of them felt that this was the time to celebrate and proceeded to do so. Higher authority heard of the party and the action taken resulted in delaying the departure of the transport.

The baggage was promptly loaded on the transport *Rawlins* and shortly before midnight everything had been happily adjusted and the entire command sailed away (August 2, 1900).

Imagine my surprise when I entered the stateroom assigned to me to find Major Walter Reed in the lower bunk. He and I were the only medical officers aboard except the transport surgeon. The Quarter-master had placed us in the same stateroom, pending permanent assignments which had been delayed until the next day by the confusion caused by the arrests. The *Rawlins* was a very small boat and could barely accommodate our command. I had the usual duties of a medical officer traveling with troops: daily sick call, and inspection of the ship with the Commanding Officer and his staff, and so forth.

Reed knew all about the affair in Havana for he had been with General Wood that afternoon but he said nothing about it until I had switched off the light and was settled in my berth. Then he said in a stern and formal way: "Doctor, were you mixed up in the celebration?"

He seemed relieved when I told him I had spent the entire day on duty at the quarantine station where our baggage was disinfected. He had always shown some interest in me since my entrance examination.

Reed was a poor sailor and he promptly dubbed the *Rawlins*, "The Rollins." However, he was on deck before I was the next morning. He had been ordered to Washington to join Dr. Victor Vaughan in completing their important report on typhoid fever. He was very anxious not to be detained at quarantine and the fact that the troops aboard came from an infected station and that most of the officers had spent the day in Havana, made him expect trouble before we reached New York. He therefore suggested to me that, during my daily inspections, I have every man who showed any signs of illness, report to the hospital where we could carefully go over him and take his temperature. He explained that in New York the quarantine officials would take the temperature of everyone and that one case running a fever which could not be explained, would hold the ship in quarantine until yellow fever could be positively excluded. If an actual case developed, it meant a delay of at least a week. By following his advice, we picked up several sick men who had not reported at sick call. All of them were easily diagnosed and a daily record of each case was kept. One of them, evidently tubercular, was running a daily afternoon temperature. This case, without a recorded study, might possibly have delayed us at quarantine.

The trip was delightful even though the sea was rough at times. Reed, a bit distressed at first, soon got his sea legs and seemed to be very happy. He was pleased with the facilities for his work at Columbia Barracks and with his quarters and associates at the hospital. He talked to me by the hour about his work and was especially delighted with the negative findings made in the bacteriological study of the blood in yellow fever cases. Agramonte's independent findings on the blood cultures agreed with those of Reed and Carroll. So this part of the Board's program was finished to Reed's great satisfaction. He had grown to be more and more optimistic about getting results with infected mosquitoes, and work on the mosquito theory was the next main objective. He was much pleased with the deep interest Lazear was showing in the mosquito work. They had had considerable difficulty in keeping mosquitoes alive for any long period at first but now they were meeting with more success and had several that were a few weeks old. (Two of Reed's mosquitoes at Camp Lazear lived sixty-five and seventy-one days, respectively, after contamination and then died of starvation as there were no volunteers at that time to feed them.) [18]

Lazear was about ready to infect some of them and to try them out on volunteers. Members of the Board, except Agramonte (an immune), had agreed to take the test. Reed had proposed this because of his apprehension about experimenting on human subjects unless members of the Board led the way. The Governor General had of course approved the Board's plans of testing Finlay's theory on volunteers, otherwise Reed would never have undertaken this dangerous procedure. He also had the support of Surgeon General Sternberg as experimenting on human subjects seemed at that time the only way of testing that theory. Since Dr. Finlay had spent years experimenting on his theory, I do not think that any member of the Board had any expectation of meeting with the sudden success which resulted from Lazear's preliminary experiments. Otherwise, Reed would have either delayed the mosquito work or had his trip to the United States postponed.

During the trip I told Major Reed that when my order came to return to the States, I had immediately sent in a request for duty in China where the Boxer

[18] Walter Reed: Baltimore address. April 1901. Senate Document No. 822, 1911, p. 101.

rebellion was in progress. He did not think that my request would be approved by the War Department but that I would be sent back to Cuba when my duty with the troops aboard was over. Because of my experience with conditions in Cuba, he thought I would be more useful to the Government if returned to Havana. We also talked of my entrance examination in 1898, and he then told me of the work he did at Professor Welch's laboratory at the Johns Hopkins Hospital in 1890–91. Dr. Abbott was taking the same course in practical bacteriology and a warm friendship developed among the trio (Welch, Reed, and Abbott).

The *Rawlins* dropped anchor off the quarantine station at Staten Island in the early evening of August 8. The quarantine launch came out and the officials looked over the surgeon's report. Then they departed, taking Major Reed with them and leaving word that they would be back in the morning. Evidently the launch came out especially for Major Reed as it was after hours at the quarantine station. The War Department, through the Surgeon General of the Army, had no doubt requested that procedure. Brigadier General C. F. Humphrey, Q. M. C., who was aboard on his way to China, was much perturbed when he saw Reed depart and he was not permitted to go with him. I was depressed.

On the morning of August 9, we were thoroughly

inspected, temperatures of everyone taken, sick men examined and then authorized to proceed. We docked at a pier in Brooklyn immediately south of the Brooklyn Bridge.

New York harbor and the city were as inspiring as ever and it was grand to be back in the U. S. A. A leave for seven days was granted to me, and before that expired, I received Special Orders No. 188, W. D., August 11, 1900 which granted me additional leave for twenty days and then directed me to proceed to San Francisco for duty with troops destined for foreign service (China or the Philippine Islands). I promptly left New York for my old home in western New York and was having a fine time there when suddenly the trouble in China ended and another order reached me revoking the previous one and directing my return to Havana.

On September 10 I sailed on the transport *Sedgwick* from New York via Newport News, Virginia (to pick up supplies), arriving in Havana late on September 17. Early on September 18 I reported to Colonel Havard who told me, much to my surprise, that I had been assigned to duty at Columbia Barracks. I was of course delighted but for a long time was much puzzled to know how it all came about. When the China rebellion collapsed, Walter Reed was in Washington and he evidently did not forget our conversation on the transport and had his way about it.

At post headquarters I was told that Captain Stark had sailed for New York with his family on September 3 on leave, but was not expected to return and that I would now be the post surgeon (see Appendix III). Captain Sickel, the Adjutant, told me that Dr. Carroll was sick with yellow fever and that there was much anxiety about the situation at the hospital.

CHAPTER EIGHT

LAZEAR—VICTOR AND MARTYR

T HE POST Adjutant provided me with transportation and I arrived at the hospital in time for a late lunch on September 18, 1900. My old friends, Drs. Pinto, de Poorter, and Ames, and two more or less strangers, Cooke and Amador, were there and joined me in the dining room. Two seats at the table, belonging to Carroll and Lazear, were vacant. All were greatly excited and lost no time in relating Lazear's success with infected mosquitoes. I was told that Lazear, Pinto, and several others had been bitten about the middle of August without results; but they also knew that Carroll and a soldier had been bitten at a later date and had developed yellow fever. Lazear, however, had not given out the details as he was undoubtedly awaiting Reed's return for such action.

Dr. Carroll was taken sick on August 31 (Appendix IV, Case 10) and was still, I believe, in the yellow fever hospital on the other side of the railroad tracks running between Quemados and La Playa. The soldier,

Private Dean, of the Seventh Cavalry, had recovered. Both of these men were known to have been bitten by Lazear's infected mosquitoes. To add to the excitement, Ames said that he had just seen Lazear, who was sick in his quarters, and that the symptoms indicated that his illness would prove to be yellow fever.

The doctors all knew that Lazear had missed several meals and that for about two days he had shown signs of distress although he continued to work and asked for no advice or help. In the early evening of September 18, Ames, Pinto, and I went to Lazear's quarters (Fig. 10, *106*), and a positive diagnosis of yellow fever was made. Ames immediately took charge and sent for one of his reliable nurses, presumably Private Nels Rasmussen, as Lambert was not available, and started treatment. Very early the next morning Ames saw Lazear and after breakfast we both saw him again. When I told Lazear that he should be in the hospital under observation, he offered no objection and he had apparently made up his own mind as to the diagnosis. In reply to questions as to the possibility that his illness might be due to mosquito infection, he was at that time rather noncommittal but admitted such a possibility. He was evidently reluctant to discuss the matter and gave us no further enlightenment. He asked me to look after his personal property.

About 10 A.M. on September 19, Lazear was carried

on a litter to our yellow fever hospital and was no doubt placed in building Number 118. Until recently I had been unable to determine, after extensive correspondence with others, in which one of these buildings he was treated. Dr. Pinto states that Carroll was sick in Number 116 and that Lazear was therefore placed in 118 as Dr. Ames did not feel that they should both be together in the same small room. I am satisfied that this is correct.

Lazear's quarters were immediately sealed up (September 19), fumigated with sulphur dioxide and then thoroughly gone over with other disinfectants in accordance with existing orders. His property was taken care of and a search was made for valuables. A small notebook was found in the blouse of the uniform he had recently worn. This and other books, papers, and so forth, were collected and secured.

Dr. Ames permitted but few visitors to the yellow fever hospital and I believe that Major Gorgas was the only one from outside of the post who was permitted to see Lazear during his illness. His case was a severe one from the beginning and he was in no condition to be questioned, but he is said to have told both Gorgas and Carroll of having been bitten by a mosquito at Las Animas Hospital. His death occurred in the evening of September 25, 1900.* The various

* See Figure 22.

authorities were notified and a cablegram sent to Mrs. Lazear from Department Headquarters.

The funeral arrangements were in my hands and unexpected difficulties were immediately encountered. Owing to the depressing effect of the numerous military funerals which had recently taken place, the Adjutant informed me that for the present it was considered best to conduct them as quietly as possible and without the services of the band. As Lazear was a contract surgeon and, as such, was entitled to but few military honors, I felt that it was wrong to make any curtailment of the usual funeral honors in his case. Captain Sickel then took me in to see the Commanding Officer who listened to my appeal and graciously consented to our program which included the band and full military honors.

All military interments from Havana, Quemados, and Columbia Barracks were made in our post cemetery located less than a quarter of a mile northwest of our hospital on the road to La Playa. This accounted for the large number of funerals mentioned. The many deaths from yellow fever in that period had been most depressing and simple funeral services, if started at an earlier date, would no doubt have been justified. In so far as I can remember, the body of Dr. Lazear was the last yellow fever case from the post or Quemados to be interred in our cemetery.

The second difficulty was encountered at the post quartermaster's office where a flag for the casket was refused. The Quartermaster had always sent flags used in yellow fever interments to the post hospital for disinfection and he informed me that they were invariably ruined and could not be reissued. Flags were not "expendable" in those days. After some discussion, a new flag was issued for the official use of the hospital. The only disinfectant that ever touched that flag was sunlight.

Finally we learned that the post chaplain would not be available to officiate at the funeral. Fortunately Dr. Ames had a friend by the name of McPherson who was a Presbyterian minister. He came out from Havana and conducted the services.

Friends from the post, officers from Department Headquarters including Major Kean, and the entire medical personnel of the hospital were present at the funeral in the afternoon of September 26. As the cemetery was but a short distance from the hospital, everyone except the nurses walked. We were able to transport the latter in ambulances. Officers, enlisted men, and nurses were all in white uniforms. Carroll, who was still sick, was unable to attend the funeral. Full military honors were accorded and it was a spontaneous demonstration of affection for our lamented friend and co-worker.

FIG. 21. Dr. Lazear's quarters. The porch was added after 1900. The great storm which swept over Western Cuba in October 1906 took off part of the roof and destroyed the big tree. The photograph was taken by Capt. William L. Little, Medical Corps, who occupied the quarters in 1906.

POST HOSPITAL, COLUMBIA BARRACKS, CUBA.

...........*Sept. 25th*...1900.

The ....*Quartermaster*...........
...........*Columbia Barracks*...........
...........*Cuba*...........

Sir;

    I have the honor to inform you that *Jesse W. Lazear*
Acting Assistant Surgeon, U.S.A............
died at this Hospital at *8:45 P.m. Sept. 25*...1900.
Di gnosis; ...*Yellow Fever*...........
Immediate cause of death;...........

       Very respectfully,

    1st Lieut.& Asst.Surgeon,U.S.Army.

      Surgeon.

FIG. 22. Facsimile of letter reporting the death of Dr. Lazear. From the original in the National Archives. (Courtesy of Dr. P. S. Hench.)

In my discussion with the Commanding Officer before the funeral, he told me of the real anxiety of the garrison over the three recent cases of yellow fever at our hospital. The numerous cases with deaths in the Quemados epidemic, and the terrible results of yellow fever when it struck General Wood's staff in Havana, were alarming. They now visualized a new epidemic starting in their own post hospital. This anxiety was of course perfectly natural. The morale of everyone was definitely shaken by the epidemics. The medical officers were discouraged and admittedly helpless in preventing epidemics of this terrible scourge. All precautions and the most thorough use of powerful disinfectants had failed. Medical men for centuries had been working in the dark, not knowing what to fight. That fact alone made yellow fever the most fearful of all diseases. Everyone considered it the pest of pests.

With the development of the three cases at the hospital from mosquito bites, the apprehension in our medical minds was immediately replaced by visions of victory. For if the mosquito were the culprit, as now seemed certain, "Yellow Jack" would lose its terrors since we believed epidemics at long last could be controlled. Victory had come to Lazear who, working entirely alone, had produced the first experimental case of yellow fever in man. He *knew* he had succeeded. Then, with real bravery and in accordance with his pledge to take the test, I firmly believe that he quietly placed a mosquito on his own arm and thereby succumbed a martyr to science. Dr. Pinto concurs in this version.

Reed, in his Baltimore address (April 1901), speaking of Lazear's service at Columbia Barracks, said:

During a service of less than one year in Cuba, he won the good will and respect of his brother officers and the affection of his immediate associates. Almost at the beginning of what promised to be a life full of usefulness and good works, he was suddenly stricken and, dying, added one more name to that imperishable roll of honor to which none other belong than martyrs to the cause of humanity.

With his death our hospital "epidemic" ended as did the general anxiety at the post. Yellow fever, except for the experimental cases from Camp Lazear, did not reappear at Columbia Barracks.

Besides being a member of the Reed Board, Lazear continued as our laboratory chief until his death. Sergeant Neate at the laboratory was carrying on as usual. The dangerous infected mosquitoes which Lazear had left were most carefully housed and taken care of by this faithful and efficient soldier.

CHAPTER NINE

THE PRELIMINARY NOTE

THE transport *Crook* with Reed aboard touched at Matanzas, Cuba, on October 3 and he learned some of the details of Lazear's death from Havard and Kean who were there on an inspection trip. In the afternoon of October 4, we all congregated on the porch to meet him. His first care was to see Carroll who was still on sick report, quite feeble, depressed and irritable. He had been sick for over a month and his convalescence was very slow and atypical of yellow fever. This was the first of the depressing circumstances which Reed soon learned.

When he rejoined our group, he was anxious to get all the details he expected from us, especially about Lazear, his death, and his mosquito experiments. He listened intently and had many questions to ask. Then he went to his laboratory and obtained from Steward Neate all the information he could give and the records showing the life history of the infected mosquitoes. Hurrying back to his quarters, he immediately began to investigate the papers obtained from Lazear's quarters. In the notebook he found the data he wanted.

Before he left Washington, he had obtained some information about the cases of Carroll and the soldier (XY); also of Lazear's illness. Thus he had become hopeful that the latter's success with mosquitoes might obviate the necessity for further experimentation on human subjects. These hopes were immediately crushed by his keen appreciation that Lazear's work was not conclusive. More and perhaps extensive experiments would be necessary to convince the world that the mosquito was responsible for the transmission of yellow fever.

He was terribly depressed at Lazear's death, not only because of his attachment and high regard for Lazear but also because this efficient assistant, having all but proved "the theory," was no longer present to help finish the work required to satisfy the medical world that the mosquito was the culprit. Age-long scientific investigations had been fruitless; Dr. Finlay's extensive experiments with infected mosquitoes had not been convincing even to his Havana confrères including Guiteras. Lazear was the only member of the board who was experienced in entomology and who had given much time to the study of mosquitoes both in the United States and in Italy. Reed realized at once how much he needed Lazear's help at that time. He wanted to know why Lazear had not promptly reported his illness to Ames. No one could tell him, but the general impression was that Lazear had not been impressed with the early symptoms and did not believe that they were due to yellow fever. Ames told him that Lazear had not felt well for a couple of days but had asked for no advice. Had he done so, he would have been placed in bed at once and the attack might have been less severe. Lazear did not work late at night as someone has stated. His notebook and the laboratory records contained the only data prepared by him, and the entries in both were no doubt made day by day as the events recorded took place. He left no message with us for Reed. From this I feel sure that he fully expected to recover. He had been in perfect health, was only 34 years old and from his extensive observation of yellow fever cases, he no doubt concluded that the chances were all in his favor. He knew that Carroll, who was 46 years old and not a robust man, was recovering, and he knew of the splendid record Dr. Ames had made in the treatment of cases in our hospital.

About this time, Reed asked for the assignment of an enlisted man to assist Steward Neate. I selected Private John H. Andrus, one of our bright and reliable men.

With the notebook and the laboratory records, Reed began his work of finding out, as nearly as possible, just what Lazear had done. It was not an easy task and it took some time. Eventually satisfied, he tabulated the findings and this resulted in the preparation of Table III which appeared in the Board's preliminary report. This table gives Lazear's results of inoculation of non-immune individuals through the bite of a mosquito, *A. egypti*. Practically all of the data for this table came from the precious notebook which Lazear had so carefully kept in his own possession.*

With the completion of Table III (Appendix IV), Reed was ready to begin a systematic study of each of the three cases. Both Carroll and Lazear had been making frequent trips to Havana but the soldier had probably not been in or near an infected area. So Reed began an intensive study of this case. This soldier was a patient in our hospital when bitten on August 31 by four of Lazear's infected mosquitoes. He was an intelligent and healthy young man, 24 years old, and not a half-wit as one might conclude from reading "Yellow Jack" by Sidney Howard. His presence in

* Shortly after this manuscript was completed word was received that a laboratory notebook 8¾ by 12½ inches with notes in the handwriting of Lazear, Reed, and possibly of Neate had been found by Laura Wood in the Library of the New York Academy of Medicine. It and other laboratory records and the small notebook of Lazear's had mysteriously disappeared after Reed's death. The laboratory book supports my recollection that the essential data were not contained in laboratory records but in a smaller notebook which Lazear kept in his own possession. It is hoped that this valuable document may also be found.—*A. E. T.*

the hospital was due to a condition (practically cured) which would in no way interfere with the test which Lazear was making. Just what Lazear said to him to gain his consent to the mosquito bites will probably never be known. I feel sure that he was told about the experiments which were being made and of the possibility of contracting yellow fever. Knowing Lazear, I cannot conceive of his doing anything underhanded to a soldier. Certainly he would not have jeopardized a man's life without telling him of the dangers and obtaining his consent. Confirming this viewpoint is the fact that the soldier never made any protest to Major Reed or to me, as Commanding Officer of the hospital, and we both had occasion to see him as will be seen below. He certainly would have told us then if he had been deceived or tricked in any way by Lazear. The dialogue in this connection in the play "Yellow Jack" is therefore misleading and extremely unfortunate. This is probably what happened: Lazear was still on duty as a member of the hospital staff. He visited all the wards in his capacity of bacteriologist. In going through this ward, he found a soldier who would soon be returned to duty and considered him an ideal young subject who could not have been exposed to yellow fever. He then probably explained his work and obtained the soldier's consent to be bitten. Lazear may have asked several patients before getting any volunteers. It will be noted in Table III that in cases 3, 5, and 11, the individuals bitten were all 24 years of age. This suggests the possibility, if not the probability, that Dean might have been bitten on August 12 (case 3), again on August 14 (case 5) and also as we positively know on August 31 (case 11) (Appendix IV).

It will be noted that the real name of this soldier was not published in the "Preliminary Note." Reed, who was of course thoroughly familiar with military procedure in such cases, realized that a slip had been made in not consulting the Post Commander before experimenting on enlisted men of his command. This had not been done and Reed decided to indicate the case as "XY" in the report and explain matters when he had more time. The soldier was Private William H. Dean of Troop "B" Seventh United States Cavalry. He was later promoted to Sergeant upon the recommendation of his Troop Commander which is definite proof that Dean was an intelligent soldier. Congress placed his name on the "Roll of Honor" with the other volunteers participating in the yellow fever experiments in Cuba. The citation by Congress states:

The case of William H. Dean was the second case of experimental yellow fever, being that which convinced the Board that the theory of its conveyance by mosquitoes was well grounded and being mentioned in their preliminary report as the case of "XY." He volunteered and was bitten August 31, 1900 by the same mosquito which had infected Major Carroll four days before. He was also bitten by two other mosquitoes which had bitten a fatal case of yellow fever twelve days before, and a fourth mosquito which had been fed on three severe cases of yellow fever. He left the military service August 17, 1902 with a character excellent and died May 3, 1928.

This case (XY) was the one which convinced Reed that the mosquito had done the trick. "XY" could not have been exposed to yellow fever while he was a patient in that particular ward. The ward surgeon, Pinto, not knowing what Lazear had done, returned the man to duty shortly after he was bitten by the infected mosquitoes. Reed was disturbed when he learned of this apparent slip for, if the soldier had been to town and exposed himself to yellow fever, the case would be as inconclusive as the others. He sent me over to the barracks to see Dean and find out what duties he had performed and where he had been after discharge from the hospital until he was again admitted as a yellow fever suspect. Dean, without hesitation, told me he had not left the post during the interval in question. I repeated the conversation to Reed and he said, "Fine."

Then, after a short time, he added, "Doctor, I must

have a talk with Private Dean myself. It's so important."

An orderly was sent for Dean, who soon reported. Major Reed, Dr. Pinto, and I were sitting on the north side of the porch. Pinto left immediately. Reed, in my presence, said:

"My man, I am studying your case of yellow fever and I want to ask you a few questions. Before questioning you, however, I will give you this ten dollar gold piece (troops were paid in gold in Cuba) if you will say that you were off this reservation at any time after you left the hospital until you returned sick with yellow fever."

Dean immediately replied, "I'm sorry, sir, but I did not leave the post at any time during that period."

Reed then asked Dean to sit down and tell him in detail everything he had done after the mosquitoes had bitten him. I withdrew and they had a long talk together. At dinner, shortly after Dean left, Reed was much elated and told us that this was a most convincing case and that he was willing to trust his reputation on it because he was so much impressed with Dean's apparent honesty and his straightforward story.

The other two cases were then taken up but in these he could not be sure of the source of the infection as both doctors had been in infected areas almost daily, before and after they had been bitten by mosquitoes.

Carroll had been bitten by a mosquito which later had also bitten Dean, and Lazear had stated that a mosquito at Las Animas Hospital had bitten him. In each case, yellow fever developed within the usual incubation period and thus strongly supported the theory. But about this time, Reed became suspicious that Lazear might also have applied infected mosquitoes to his own arm. The more he pondered over this idea, the more convinced he became. However, he was not sure and was much troubled as to what to say about this case.

I have a distinct recollection that there were some notations in Lazear's notebook which Reed thought were entries about mosquitoes which Lazear had applied to himself. Reed was cautious about discussing this aspect of Lazear's case, but he did confide in me and possibly discussed it with Carroll and Agramonte. Reed believed that when Lazear was taken sick, he worried lest his life insurance become forfeited if it became known that he had deliberately infected himself with a fatal disease. Was this the reason for Lazear's incomplete entries about himself in the notebook? Did he withhold facts to protect his dear ones at this critical moment? Was this why he told Gorgas and Carroll the story about his having been bitten by a mosquito at Las Animas Hospital? Reed believed it was. A competent scientific investigator who had al-

ready produced two cases of yellow fever, Lazear
certainly would not knowingly let any mongrel
mosquito bite him at a yellow fever hospital, especially
when he *then knew* the danger. He was after information of tremendous importance and the only way to
get it was to be bitten by one of his own thoroughbred
"birds" which had been hatched and infected under
his own supervision.

But there was no way for Reed to prove this viewpoint and so the "Preliminary Note" simply gave
the story of the supposed infection by a mosquito at
Las Animas Hospital. Lazear had been making almost
daily visits there to infect mosquitoes on new cases of
yellow fever and Reed finally decided to let it appear
that he was accidentally infected while in the per-
formance of his official duties as a member of the
Board, a possibility of course, but all of us at the
hospital were convinced that Lazear had placed the
mosquitoes on his own arm just as he did on Carroll in
accordance with the agreement of the non-immune
members of the Board.

Carroll, in his Galveston address, tells of Lazear's
statement to him:

Dr. Lazear was applying mosquitoes as usual late in the
afternoon to patients in the yellow fever hospital known
as "Las Animas" and, while thus engaged, a mosquito
alighted upon his hand. He allowed it to take its fill and

concluded it was one of the *common culex mosquitoes* which were present in the hospital in large numbers. So little importance did he attach to the incident that he made no note of it and related the incident to me when first taken sick five days afterward.

If, as I believe, Carroll was still convalescing in one of the huts of the yellow fever hospital when Lazear was admitted, the conversation could have taken place there. In this same connection, I wish to record a discussion I had with my esteemed friend, the late Dr. Henry R. Carter. I was calling on him at his residence in Washington, D. C., in March 1922. He was then writing a book on the "History of Yellow Fever" and was interested in what I might be able to tell him about this particular matter. He wanted to show me a letter from Major Gorgas to Mrs. Gorgas written during Lazear's illness—or just after his death—but could not find it. A few days later, I received a letter from him which I still have, quoting from the Gorgas letter as follows:

Lazear told me that he saw a mosquito, which he believes to have been the *one they are investigating*, on his hand at Las Animas Hospital and he let him bite as long as he wanted to.

So far as I know, these are the only statements made by Lazear during his illness about the source of his infection. The italics in the two statements above are mine. Notice the contradictory remarks about the mosquito involved. *Culex pungens* * was probably as prevalent in Havana as any other mosquito. Lazear would have known which one had bitten him.

In order to confirm my recollection of these important events, I asked Dr. Pinto (September 1941) for a statement and here is his reply:

The story that Lazear allowed a mongrel mosquito to bite him at Las Animas Hospital is fantastic. *Reed discussed it with me.* You and I, as well as Ames, were certain that Lazear was hiding something regarding his infection. He already had had two cases and in his own mind was certain that the mosquito was the intermediary host. Regarding the place where Dean was bitten, it is my opinion that it must have been done in the ward. Dean was a bed patient at that time. I was the ward surgeon and Dean was the only patient in the ward. It was much easier to bring the mosquitoes to the ward than it would have been to have the patient go to the laboratory. The mosquito was applied to my own arm on August 25th by Lazear on the porch of our quarters (Building 108). The mosquito was brought in a test tube. Besides Lazear, Carroll and Ames were present.

This chapter was written long before the information in the preceding paragraph was received from Dr.

* The mosquito we called *Culex pungens* in Cuba at that time was probably *C. quinquefaciatus.*

Pinto. As it definitely confirms all of my recollections of what was told me on September 18, 1900, Dr. Pinto's statement has been inserted without rewriting the chapter.

The result of the bite by the infected mosquito in Pinto's case was negative. Dr. Carroll, bitten two days later (August 27) also by one infected mosquito, developed a severe case of yellow fever (Appendix IV). He had a wife and five small children at his home in Washington and he had every right to face the requirements of his pledge with much trepidation, although it was generally known that he had little or no faith in the mosquito theory at that time.

With a complete record of these three cases (Carroll, Dean, and Lazear) before him, and the probability that all three were contracted from bites of Lazear's laboratory-bred mosquitoes, Reed concluded that the results must be published at once. His reason for haste in making public these preliminary and most likely unacceptable experiments was that he was apprehensive that the British scientists who had visited him in July and who were probably working along the same lines, might also get immediate results. The Reed Board had spent almost two months doing bacteriological work to complete their investigations on the Sanarelli organism before pursuing the mosquito theory vigorously. Reed and Lazear were, however, raising mosquitoes and learning how to care for them and keep them alive early in July. Consequently, Drs. Durham and Meyers, if they had promptly started to investigate the mosquito theory with what they had learned in the laboratory, might have been first in telling the world of successful results.

Reed, who like all true scientists, was habitually accurate, slow and deliberate, now became a whirlwind of activity. He hurriedly wrote a rough draft of his ideas and conclusions, read it over to Kean and all the rest of us. The report was the one subject of discussion among us. Criticism was invited. Optimism reigned among the younger officers and Reed, who felt the same way, had to call on his more mature experience and restrict himself to facts and eliminate opinions. He fully realized that the three cases in the report were *not* conclusive and would not satisfy a skeptical world that they had proved anything, although he was personally convinced that he now could produce the proof required within a short period of time. He was therefore very careful in stating his conclusions and in the final draft eliminated anything which might be considered radical. It is interesting to note that his statements have withstood the test of time.

All of the work of compiling the Board's report was done in the front (north) room of Reed's quarters on one of the Medical Department's folding, field mess tables. This was a sturdy oak table with dimensions about 3 by 7 feet. A Medical Department field desk occupying one end of this table contained all his papers. For a few days, Reed worked early and late on the report, rewriting parts which did not satisfy him. He did it all with a pen as no stenographers were available. The final typing was done at Department Headquarters at Quemados by one of the civilian clerks, probably John J. Moran.

Since Carroll was sick and Agramonte absent, the work of preparing the report fell almost entirely to the president of the Board, Walter Reed. I hope that no one will infer from the relating of these circumstances that I desire to detract in any way from the credit due each member of the Board for the results obtained. All of them did their duties as prescribed by Reed, and the glory of the achievement belongs to them all. The protracted illness of Carroll was a great blow to Reed for he needed this tried and efficient assistant badly at this time. Great glory was added to this historical achievement *because the first experimental case developed in a member of the Board— Carroll.* In this connection, too, *Lazear's martyrdom* should not be forgotten. It was also no fault of Agramonte's if he took advantage of a leave of absence while Reed was in the States. For many years I have wondered why I did not see Dr. Agramonte at our hospital from September 18, the day I returned there, until about October 8. Reed returned October 4 as will be remembered. I could not recall the reason for Agramonte's absence until Dr. P. S. Hench sent me Dr. Hammeter's article [19] on Dr. Carroll's work. That article quotes several of Dr. Carroll's letters to his wife and in the one dated September 23, 1900, he states in effect that Dr. Agramonte and his wife left for New York the day before. If that statement is correct, it would explain many important things.

Nearly all of these letters of Carroll give glowing accounts of his rapid progress toward recovery. Among other things he tells of doing an autopsy, a feat which he could not possibly have performed even as late as his return from leave in November. His object evidently was to relieve the anxiety of his wife and children at home. Reed was still in Washington when some of those letters were received, knew their contents and was therefore unprepared to find, on October 4, that his chief assistant was still a very ill man. He promptly took steps to send Carroll to his home in Washington on sick leave. Dr. Pinto took a short leave and went with Carroll at Reed's request.

While working on the report, Reed was arranging with the Surgeon General for his return to the United States to read it at a meeting of the Public Health

[19] *Janus*, 1908, pp. 164–165.

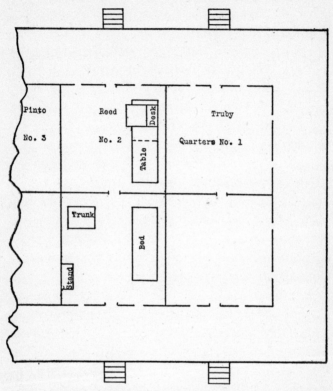

FIG. 23. Plan of Major Reed's quarters (building No. 108) at Columbia Barracks. The sets were assigned at that time as follows: (1) Lieutenant Truby, (2) Major Reed, (3) Dr. Pinto, (4) Dr. Carroll, (5) Dr. Ames. Drs. Amador and Cooke shared quarters with Drs. Pinto and Ames.

Association at Indianapolis. He was also planning the future work of the Board which would be necessary to prove the theory. By October 12, the report was practically finished, and on that date Reed and Kean drove to Havana in General Lee's carriage, which Kean had borrowed for the purpose. En route, Kean suggested that he ask General Wood for money to pay for the experiments and also to pay a gratuity for any Spanish immigrants who would volunteer to take the tests. General Wood promptly approved these requests and obtained the Spanish Consul's approval of experimenting on his countrymen provided they volunteered and received the gratuity which was offered, and were of age to be free from parental control which in Spain was the rather mature age of 24 years. Some of the first volunteers were under that age and were promptly released.

On October 14, just ten days after returning to Cuba, Reed was again on his way to the United States with the finished report of the Board entitled "The Etiology of Yellow Fever, a Preliminary Note." It was read by Reed in person at the meeting of the American Public Health Association at Indianapolis, Indiana, October 22 to 26, 1900, and was published in the *Philadelphia Medical Journal*, October 27, 1900.

As Reed had expected, critics at once attacked the members of the Board, especially Reed, and tried to discredit the report. The conservative members of the medical profession were silent and probably skeptical or at least not very optimistic.

Dr. Wasdin of the Marine Hospital Service, a strong supporter of the Sanarelli theory, published a scathing attack in the November 17 issue of the *Philadelphia Medical Journal*. Reed said nothing. After the meeting, Reed went to Washington, saw the Surgeon General and Carroll (on sick leave) and then immediately returned to Havana.

The following letter from Major Reed to General Sternberg is of interest.[20]

INDIANAPOLIS, IND., *Oct. 22, 1900*

DEAR GENERAL STERNBERG:

Just as I was leaving the city, I dropped you a postal suggesting that the words "with his full consent" be erased in the cases of Carroll (page 12) and Lazear (page 20), as their absence from the history of T. C. Y. might attract attention and lead to the inference that his inoculation was done without his consent . . . I will also ask that you will turn to the last page of MSS. (22) beginning "since we here," etc. Let the first paragraph stand as it is but change the rest as follows:

From our study thus far of yellow fever, we draw the following conclusions:

[20] George Miller Sternberg: A Biography. American Medical Association, 1920, p. 221.

1. Bacillus icteroides (Sanarelli) stands in no causative relation to yellow fever, but, when present, should be considered as a secondary invader in this disease.

2. The mosquito serves as the intermediate host for the parasite of yellow fever.

Strike out the remainder "and it is highly probable that" etc., as this is merely an expression of opinion which may turn out to be right or wrong. Future observations can only determine this point—of course, conclusions 1 and 2 in your copy are to be erased entirely . . .

The initials "T. C. Y." were evidently intended for "XY." I doubt if the question regarding Dean's consent had arisen while Reed was writing the report in Cuba and I also doubt if he had asked Dean that question. At Indianapolis he saw that the inference mentioned might arise and this was the only way to avoid it. The extreme care taken in writing the "conclusions" is well shown.

CHAPTER TEN

CAMP LAZEAR

REED was back with us early in November and started at once to carry out the plans he had formulated for establishing an isolated camp, which was to be called Camp Lazear and to be a place where the experiments could be made along scientific lines. He was ready to show that the mosquito could transmit the disease to men living away from infected areas and under a strictly enforced quarantine. This would eliminate the criticisms that followed the preliminary experiments. His first move was to see General Wood in Havana.

Our principal means of transportation for officers at that time was the "Dougherty wagon" of Indian War days. Reed had ridden hundreds of miles in these wagons while serving with troops on the western plains. He still seemed to get a thrill riding in one behind four good, lively army mules. He made frequent trips to Havana in them and usually took one of us along for company. On this occasion he asked me to accompany him as he wanted to arrange for equip-

ment for the camp and depended on me to tell the
Chief Quartermaster what supplies could not be provided at the hospital. He knew exactly what he
wanted.

The Dougherty wagon was waiting for us after
breakfast, the day after Reed returned from the States.
The ride to Havana in the early morning was a very
pleasant one and our driver took us at a lively clip. We
were promptly admitted to the Governor General's
office and there was a very cordial greeting between
the two officers. Reed told of his trip to Indianapolis
and the rather skeptical reception of his paper. This
did not dampen the enthusiasm of either one of them
and Reed was confident that he could promptly prove
the mosquito theory. He related the plans to establish
a camp near Columbia Barracks as soon as possible.
General Wood concurred and promised his full support. We then went to see Major Chauncey B. Baker,
Chief Quartermaster, who had recently succeeded
Brigadier General C. F. Humphrey to that office. He
was intensely interested and promised speedy action
on plans for construction as well as for equipment.
Reed wanted new tentage and new field equipment, in
original packages if possible, so that the danger of in-
troducing infected articles could be eliminated. Major
Baker stated that new equipment was available and
would be provided.

The Governor General's staff was ready to do anything to help solve the yellow fever problem. The recent epidemic in Havana had been terribly severe among their personnel. Five of the officers on General Wood's staff had contracted the disease and of these Major Cartwright, Major Peterson, and Captain Page had died; of forty-eight civilian employees stricken, seven had perished. These officers and employees had been living in the cleanest and best sections of Havana, and General Wood, commenting on the thorough cleaning the city had had during the past year under General Ludlow's personal supervision, was convinced that yellow fever was not a "filth disease." The effect of this epidemic on the personnel of the staff is best described in General Baker's own words. He was a patient at the Walter Reed Hospital in 1935 while I was in command of the Army Medical Center and we enjoyed reminiscing, as old timers are supposed to do, about our service together in Havana. At that time he said he would send me a typewritten copy of remarks he had made at a luncheon in 1934, and he urged me to write up my own experiences, stating that I could quote whatever I wished from his article. The following is an extract:

In August 1900, I had become the Chief Quartermaster of the Department of Cuba—General Humphrey, my predecessor, having been ordered to duty in China.* I oc-

* General Humphrey sailed from Havana August 2 on the S.S. *Rawlins.—A. E. T.*

cupied for my office the building then known as the Segundo Cabo, facing the Plaza on which was located the Governor General's Palace. In this same building were located the offices of Chief Paymaster and Chief Commissary. In a vacant room on the second floor of this building we organized a small mess, where we served our luncheons. There were eight people who were members of this mess, including my principal assistant, Major George Cartwright; Major Matt Peterson, Chief Commissary Officer; Mrs. Peterson, his wife; Captain Page, an aide-de-camp to the Commanding General; Colonel Dodge, the Chief Paymaster; Lieutenants Hanna and E. C. Brooks, aides-de-camp to the Commanding General. The earliest deaths from yellow fever during this epidemic occurred outside the limits of Havana, at Pinar del Rio and Marianao. The first of this group at mess to go down with yellow fever was Major George Cartwright, my principal assistant, who died of the disease. Sitting at his left was Major Peterson, who went down with the disease and died. . . . On the next day, as I followed this funeral to the last resting place, a carriage ahead of me turned out and I paused long enough to speak with the occupant, Captain Page, who informed me that he was so ill he could not proceed. I told him I would go on to the funeral and as soon as I got back would get in touch with him. Page occupied quarters at the top story of Segundo Cabo. When I returned to my office I found him there, unable to climb the stairs to his quarters and with help I assisted him to his room at the top of the building. Within 48 hours he died of yellow fever. The next to be stricken with the disease was Colonel Dodge, Chief Paymaster of the Department. Fortunately he recovered and later became Paymaster General of the Army. The next place at the table was vacant as Lieutenant Hanna had taken a leave of absence and returned to the United States. That left Captain E. C. Brooks and me looking across the corner of the table at one another.

At the advice of the surgeons, we had been in the habit of serving a small quantity of red wine at luncheon. Some one of the group, at the early inception of the epidemic, had proposed the old English toast: "To those who are gone already and here's to the next to go." This toast was drunk daily until Brooks and I were left looking across the corner of the table at one another. Then, when he poured out a glass of wine and pushed the decanter to me, he lifted his glass and gave the toast. I remember saying: "Brooks, I won't drink that toast to myself. You had yellow fever in Santiago and are immune and won't have it again. Besides that, you are a teetotaler and don't drink. So I'll drink my wine but not the toast." He laughed and neither he nor I was stricken with the disease.

During the same period, one after the other, I placed five men in charge of Major Cartwright's papers which I was anxious should be closed up as promptly as possible, especially in view of the conditions that existed. In order to make sure that they would be promptly closed and worked upon continuously, I set aside a small room back of my own office and I assigned a clerk to this special duty. The first that I placed in charge was Mr. Ferguson, a civilian clerk, supposed to be immune, having passed through more than one epidemic in New Orleans. Within 24 hours after he took charge of the papers, he came to me and said he was too ill to go on. The next day he was dead of yellow fever. One after the other, five men working on these papers went down with yellow fever. The fifth man went down but fortunately recovered and finished the papers.

The next thing on Reed's program was to find a suitable camp site far enough away from habitations to insure complete isolation and at the same time in the vicinity of Columbia Barracks. Such a site was promptly found southeast of our hospital and about one mile distant by road on the *finca* (farm) of Señor Rojas. The hospital personnel took great interest in the construction of this camp. Our detachment, under Acting Stewards Claude M. Cook and George Burton, erected the tents and did all the work except the construction of the two wooden buildings which were built by the Quartermaster Department with Cuban labor. Reed gave minute attention to all the details and thoroughly enjoyed the work. He personally drew up all the plans for the two buildings and watched the construction most carefully. The wire screening used on doors and windows was extremely fine, 0.5 mm. mesh. Every possible step was taken to make sure that no mosquito could find an opening in either building large enough for its passage. Tongue and grooved lumber was used; and all doors and windows were most carefully fitted. Cracks on the outside of the building were covered by strips of wood. Building No. 1 * was equipped for experimenting with infected clothing and bedding. It had but two small windows, both on the south (front) side of the house. Poor ventilation was desired in this building. Building Number 2 was used for conducting experiments with infected mosquitoes. It was purposely very well ventilated and equipped with new, uncontaminated supplies. A description of these buildings was given in the Board's report, "An additional note on the Etiology of Yellow Fever."

When Reed returned from Washington, he brought with him a packing box (capacity about 5 cu. ft.) filled with literature on yellow fever, from the Surgeon General's Library. He also had recent pamphlets furnished by Dr. L. O. Howard of the Department of Agriculture. This literature kept him busy evenings.

* In 1941 Dr. Philip S. Hench, with Mr. John J. Moran and Mr. Luis Pogolotti of Havana, located the site of Camp Lazear. Building No. 1 was still there on its original foundations. Building No. 2 was not there, having been destroyed by a tropical hurricane some time after 1906.

The two big volumes by La Roche on yellow fever were constantly consulted and he would frequently interrupt his young companions who were usually playing games or otherwise amusing themselves on the porch, with something like this: Gentlemen! Listen to what La Roche says about the terrible epidemic in Philadelphia in 1793. Then he would read and get us all interested. A discussion usually followed. On other evenings, he would draw us all into a study and discussion of the mosquito pamphlets. Soon he had us collecting mosquitoes with a large-mouthed cyanide bottle. These specimens we would study with strong hand lenses and he would check them over. When one was found which we could not identify, off it would go by mail to Howard in Washington. The importance of mosquito control and the most practicable methods of destroying these insects and preventing their breeding were not neglected. Major Kean had, after Lazear's mosquito experiments, been so impressed with the importance of mosquito control work that on October 13, 1900, he recommended official action by the Department Commander. Circular No. 8, Headquarters Department of Western Cuba, was issued two days later (October 15) requiring action by post commanders. This was the first of these important orders in Cuba (Appendix V). Then we put these methods to a practical test at our post with remarkable effect. Reed, the great teacher, was doing his young associates a great service: and so was Kean, the practical sanitarian.

Shortly before the middle of November 1900, one of the severe tropical storms which are so common in Cuba at this season hit our part of the island with great fury. High winds with rain, first from the south and later from the north, did great damage. Trees were uprooted and things not securely anchored were blown away. On November 13, Reed wrote: "It is now 62° with a strong northwest wind." Mosquitoes were destroyed or blown out to sea. Walter Reed was worried. At lunch time, about November 15, he told us that most of his laboratory bred mosquitoes had died and that he had but few of the dry eggs left to start a new crop. He was apprehensive too that the destruction of infected mosquitoes by the storm would end the epidemic in Havana. With all these adverse conditions, he was fearful that he would not be able to get prompt results such as Lazear had obtained in the hot months of August and September. Those of us who had been through such storms in Cuba, reassured him that it would soon warm up and that mosquitoes or their eggs could always be found. But he said, in effect: I have been unable to find any mosquitoes and I must have them right away for the camp is almost ready to operate. It may be weeks before we can get started.

We could not relieve his anxiety by talking, so after

lunch several of us started out for Quemados. The quartermaster warehouses and a large dump for condemned property were passed on the way and so we stopped to see if any of the many containers (galvanized iron cans, buckets, scrap iron, drain pipes, and the like) held any water. Many of these articles had the inspector's axe holes in the bottoms to indicate that they had been condemned. We found water in some of them in spite of the holes. A few mosquitoes were seen as can after can was pulled out of the heap. Soon we came across a galvanized can so inclined that it held some water. Carefully extracting it, we saw many of the beautiful, lyre-marked *A. aegypti* escape. In that can and a few other containers, enough larvae and eggs were found to supply the laboratory for some time. We went right back to the laboratory where Reed, Neate, and Andrus secured the "wigglers" and picked out the eggs with great glee. The latter, some about ready to hatch, were placed in water in screened containers and others, quite fresh, were dried out for future use. In order to check my memory on this matter, I wrote to J. H. Andrus in 1940, and here is his reply:

I recall the storm and cold weather which resulted in our mosquito famine very distinctly. I remember that the Major was nearly frantic when you prospectors discovered the mosquito mine. There is just one thing to add: Before those cans were fixed so they would hold no more rain water, I made many trips with dipper and buckets collecting pupae and larvae for our sanctuary. It was not a nice job. The cans in which we got the richest hauls had been used for toilets before the sewage system was put in. All this led the Major to conclude that the filthier the environment, the healthier the mosquito.

As previously stated, Dr. Finlay provided the mosquito eggs at the beginning of the Board's work. Lazear could easily have added to the supply if he had needed them at any time. Incidentally, the finding of the mosquitoes in the quartermaster dump resulted in a good jolt for the sanitary officer. The post commander took prompt steps on the recommendation of the Medical Department, to have the conditions at the dump corrected and at about the same time directed extensive mosquito control work on the entire military reservation in compliance with Circular No. 8. Yellow Fever, at the post, except for the experimental cases, ended then and there.

The following letter confirms the state of the weather, and other important details, including the date of Carroll's return to duty with the Board: [21]

Major Reed to General Sternberg:

[21] George Miller Sternberg: A Biography. American Medical Association, 1920, p. 222.

COLUMBIA BARRACKS, QUEMADOS, CUBA
November 13, 1900

MY DEAR GENERAL STERNBERG:

. . . My voyage down was fairly pleasant although I was as usual a victim to sea sickness. I have been very busy trying to get our experimental station started. Have secured a good location and hope to have the detachment go out on Thursday, 15th. I have already had three candidates to offer themselves for the mosquito inoculations and will have no difficulty in getting subjects for the infected bedding and clothing experiments. (I hope that you will not mention this to anyone.) The difficulty before us now will be largely due to the marked change in the temperature. It is now 62°—with a strong northwest wind. Has been cold ever since I arrived. As the result of this past week's cool weather, cases have dropped from 100 to 76, and I suppose we may expect a still further reduction in about 5 to 7 days. If it were only August 1, everything would be plain sailing but I foresee that we will be much handicapped by the weather.

We will have our small experimental buildings heated if necessary, and in that way, hope to counteract the outside temperature.

Dr. Carroll arrived this afternoon and will at once take up the work.

On November 10, Dr. Pinto left us for the United States just as the camp was about ready to be occupied. A few Spanish volunteers were preparing to move in.

Men were required at the camp for various duties and we were asked to select reliable and intelligent men from the hospital detachment. As I had been at the hospital off and on for over a year, I knew them well. We discussed the qualifications required for each position to be filled. Each man was questioned and asked if he wanted to serve at the camp. All accepted. Reed did not ask any of the enlisted men to volunteer for the test. Imagine his surprise when one of them, Private John R. Kissinger, said he would like to volunteer. This bold step by one of the most reliable members of the detachment was a stirring and unforgettable event.

Even at this early date, Reed was experiencing doubts about success with the Spaniards for difficulties had already been encountered. Kissinger's unsolicited action therefore impressed him greatly and bolstered his depressed spirits. A day or two later, he was fairly beaming when he told us that John J. Moran, a civilian clerk, at General Lee's headquarters, had also volunteered. Other members of the detachment of the Hospital Corps soon followed the example of Kissinger and Moran and before the experiments were finished, twelve (thirteen with Cooke) had volunteered, taken the tests, and nine had developed the disease. Three of them, after living in the infected bedding building for twenty-one days, volunteered for the mosquito test and contracted yellow fever. One of them, Warren G.

Jernegan, after the fomite and mosquito tests had both failed to infect him, bravely took the blood inoculation test and promptly had the attack of yellow fever he seemed so bent on having. If it were possible to select an outstanding hero among these heroes, Jernegan's name would certainly have to be considered. All of the men had been through the typhoid epidemics of the recent war with Spain; had witnessed the horrors of the yellow fever epidemics in Havana and Quemados; were cognizant of all that had transpired in our own yellow fever wards; and knew all the details of the experimental cases of Carroll, "XY," and Lazear. They were of excellent character, above average in intelligence, and knew full well what might happen to them if they were bitten by infected mosquitoes. Yet they volunteered and some of them even refused the gratuity which was offered. As Reed said of Kissinger:[22] "In my opinion, this exhibition of moral courage has never been surpassed in the annals of the Army of the United States."

On February 28, 1929, Congress placed the names of all of the volunteers on the "Roll of Honor" together with those of the members of the Board. Their names with citations are published annually in the Official Army Register.

While Reed would not ask our enlisted men to

[22] Walter Reed: Baltimore Address, April 1901. Senate Document No. 822, 61st Congress, 1911, p. 98.

volunteer for the mosquito bites, he did not hesitate
to ask them to undergo the infected bedding test. He
asked the youngest doctor on our staff, Contract
Surgeon Robert P. Cooke, if he would take charge of
the infected clothing and bedding building and live in
it with other volunteers. Cooke promptly accepted.
He was a young Virginian and Reed was very fond of
him. Cooke had come to us from the First Infantry at
Pinar del Rio, pending result of a recommendation to
the War Department that his contract be annulled as
he was one of the doctors at Pinar del Rio during the
recent yellow fever epidemic which the local doctors
had diagnosed as pernicious malaria. Reed had investigated that epidemic and had strongly opposed the
discharge of Cooke as the latter was a new arrival at
the post during the epidemic and had nothing to do
with the diagnosis and treatment of the yellow fever
cases. So after Cooke volunteered for the work at
Camp Lazear, Reed wrote to the Surgeon General:

I have to ask as a special favor that Acting Assistant
Surgeon, R. P. Cooke, who so courageously volunteered
to take charge of our terribly infected yellow fever building No. 1, may not have his contract annulled, but be sent
to the Philippines, if he cannot remain in Cuba.

His contract was not annulled and he continued to
serve in the Army for four years longer. Reed delighted in teasing Cooke in a friendly way and at such

times pronounced his name as "Cookie." Two of our fine enlisted men, Folk and Jernegan, joined Cooke and lived in the infected bedding building for twenty days. Both of these men then took the other tests and both developed yellow fever. This, after knowing that while they were caged up in the "filth house," several of their companions had developed yellow fever in the scrupulously clean "mosquito house"— Heroes! Yes! Real ones!

While Walter Reed was somewhat doubtful, even worried, about getting prompt results with mosquitoes during the cold spell, he was happy and strictly in his element in planning and getting the camp equipped and organized. Long army experience made it a simple matter for him to get action. It was not *red tape* to him. With the full support of the highest authorities, his every request was promptly forthcoming. Reed was particularly happy in this part of the work and supervised all details personally. I am sure he would have done this, no matter how many assistants he might have had. The facilities of the post hospital, with its personnel and equipment, were always available and proved a great asset to the work of the Board.

When Carroll returned from sick leave on November 13, the camp was practically finished. During November, Agramonte came frequently to discuss the

plans with his chief and it is quite probable that while
the camp was in process of construction, he was infecting mosquitoes in preparation for the work that was to
follow. On this point, I have no positive information.
It must be remembered that Agramonte had two important positions. During the entire period of the
Board's work, he was in charge of the large Department laboratory. He was a very busy man, well qualified in pathology and bacteriology. Being a native of
Cuba and presumably an immune, he did nearly all of
the Army's autopsy work in Havana and vicinity. His
qualifications in that work were no doubt considered
when he was selected to serve as a member of the
Board. All other members were non-immune. Agramonte held his position at the Department laboratory
continuously during the occupation of Cuba by United
States troops. The importance of his work there no
doubt kept Reed from asking for his full time duty
with the Board.

Shortly before the camp was opened, Reed was
concerned with the problem of its management. He
wanted a commissioned officer to live in camp to en-
sure order and see that the guard was efficiently carrying out orders. Carroll was being reserved for other
and more important work in line with his qualifications. Reed unfolded his plans to me in a serious discussion of the matter. Unforeseen circumstances,

however, arose to interfere with his plans and, as the yellow fever hospital was inactive at the time, Ames was selected to run the camp. Later, when experimental cases of the disease developed, they were promptly transferred to the yellow fever hospital where Ames treated them. However, he continued to live in a tent at Camp Lazear. During the discussion mentioned, Reed told me of his determination to take the mosquito test as soon as he was sure that the results were well established and he could be spared from the work.

Camp Lazear was opened on November 20, 1900. The volunteers, Kissinger, Moran and several Spaniards, were placed in isolation at the camp. Every man who took part in the tests was required to sign a statement showing that he voluntarily offered himself for the yellow fever experiments and that he absolved the Government from any claims. Carroll, who returned for duty on November 13, was obviously still unable to do any hard work or live in camp and Reed would not let him do anything which would retard his complete recovery. He was therefore put in charge of the mosquito work. This included taking the insects to Las Animas Hospital, infecting them on new cases of yellow fever, caring for them and making records. This work imposed no great physical strain.

By November 30, five volunteers had each been bitten once and some twice after three day intervals, without results. Reed said in his report that this "was somewhat disturbing" but attributed the failure to the cool weather.

Reed, in the following personal letter to General Sternberg on November 26, referred to the conditions which were giving him some anxiety.[23]

Major Reed to General Sternberg:

November 26, 1900

. . . At this writing, the experimental station is nearly completed and we have already begun on our observations. We have several individuals, American and Spanish, willing to take bites or blood injections, and we hope to be able to decide some of the vexed questions in the etiology of this disease. We anticipate considerable trouble concerning the rearing of our mosquitoes during this cooler weather. Unless we can keep them alive from eighteen to twenty-four days after the infection, we could not expect positive results, since it required twelve to sixteen days in the hotter weather of August to enable them to convey the disease. Some of the Havana papers, especially *La Discussion,* have abused us soundly and have charged us with all kinds of inhumanity and barbarity; but since the Spanish consul, a most courteous and intelligent gentleman, assures us that we shall have his support, as long as we do not use minors and the individual gives his written consent, I am not at all disturbed by these newspaper attacks . . .

[23] George Miller Sternberg: A Biography. American Medical Association, 1920, p. 222.

1. 1st Lieut. A. E. Truby, Comdg. Detachment *
2. Alvah S. Pinto, Contract Surgeon
3. Raoul Amador, Contract Surgeon
4. Robert P. Cooke, Contract Surgeon
5. Acting Hospital Steward Campbell
6. A. H. S. Pahnke
7. A. H. S. George Burton
8. A. H. S. Claude M. Cook
9. A. H. S. Arnold
10. Pvt. John R. Kissinger
11. Pvt. Braemer
12. Pvt. Thomas Kane
13. Pvt. De Lamar
14. Pvt. Kneisley
15. Pvt. John Morris
16. Pvt. Lawrence
17. Pvt. William Olsen
18. Pvt. Samillion
19. Pvt. Carr
20. Pvt. Martin
21. Pvt. William McHardy
22. Pvt. Gustave Lambert
23. Pvt. Tate
24. Pvt. Thomas M. England
25. Pvt. John H. Andrus
26. Pvt Harroldsen
27. Pvt. Clyde L. West
28. Pvt. Brent La Mar
29. Pvt. James Toler
30. Pvt. Thomas Brault
31. Pvt. Frank Buholtz
32. Pvt. James Byington
33. Pvt. William Williamson
34. Pvt. Young
35. Pvt. Springer
36. Pvt. Rutledge
37. Pvt. William Roberton
38. Pvt. Courtney
39. Pvt. Frank M. Dawley
40. Pvt. John Colby
41. Pvt. Charles G. Sontag

This detachment furnished most of the volunteers for the experiments on yellow fever made at Camp Lazear.

VOLUNTEERS

4. Dr. Robert P. Cooke
10. Pvt. John R. Kissinger
17. Pvt. William Olsen
24. Pvt. Thomas M. England
25. Pvt. John H. Andrus
41. Pvt. Charles G. Sontag

VOLUNTEERS NOT SHOWN IN PHOTOGRAPH BUT MEMBERS OF SAME DETACHMENT

Pvt. Levi E. Folk
Pvt. Wallace W. Forbes
Pvt. James L. Hanberry
Pvt. James Hildebrand
Pvt. Warren G. Jernegan
Pvt. Edward Weatherwalks

* This Detachment had previously been commanded by Capt. A. N. Stark.

FIG. 24. The Detachment Hospital Corps, Columbia Barracks, September 1900.

FIG. 25. The hospital, Rowell Barracks, Cuba, 1900.

CHAPTER ELEVEN

"THE THEORY IS ALL RIGHT"

THE policy of the Chief Surgeon was to have a commissioned medical officer at each military station of any size. The shortage of regular officers was more acute than ever and, as Captain Stark returned to duty quite unexpectedly, I became available to fill the position of Post Surgeon at Rowell Barracks, Paso Caballos, near Cienfuegos, Cuba.

There had been considerable yellow fever in the city of Cienfuegos but none at the post. However, much malaria had been reported at that station and they now had a case suspicious of being yellow fever. This of course indicated the possibility that something like the Pinar del Rio incident might be taking place there. Walter Reed was keenly interested from a professional standpoint and also because his son, Lawrence, a second lieutenant in the Tenth Infantry, was stationed there. While I was making preparations to leave, he utilized every available opportunity to discuss my new duties. He urged me to start the fight against mosquitoes promptly. "Do it thoroughly, don't forget

the Q. M. dump" was one of his parting reminders.
He also asked me to send him specimens of the prevailing mosquitoes. While he knew that *Culex fasciatus*
(*A. aegypti*) and *Culex pungens* were the most common mosquitoes in and around Havana, he wanted
some first-hand information on that point about other
yellow fever centers in Cuba.

My duty at Columbia Barracks ended on November
30, 1900. I left Havana that morning by train and
reported at my new station the same afternoon. The
command consisted of Headquarters, band, and one
battalion of the Tenth United States Infantry. It took
a few days to get a good, clear picture of my new job
but I very soon became convinced that while yellow
fever at Cienfuegos would certainly become epidemic
if the non-immune population were large, it would be
an easy matter (based on the mosquito theory) to
keep the Army post from becoming infected.

The post, Rowell Barracks, was located on the east
bank of the narrow entrance to the large and magnificent harbor. The city, six miles away, could be reached
only by boat. There were no dwellings within miles
of us on our side of the bay. The post was on a rocky
surface sloping sharply to the shores of the inlet with
almost perfect natural drainage. An artesian well
furnished the fine water which was piped to barracks
and quarters. Storm waters and sewage were conducted

Fig. 26. Facsimile of Walter Reed's letter to Lieutenant Truby, which seems to be the first written account of his first experimental case of yellow fever.

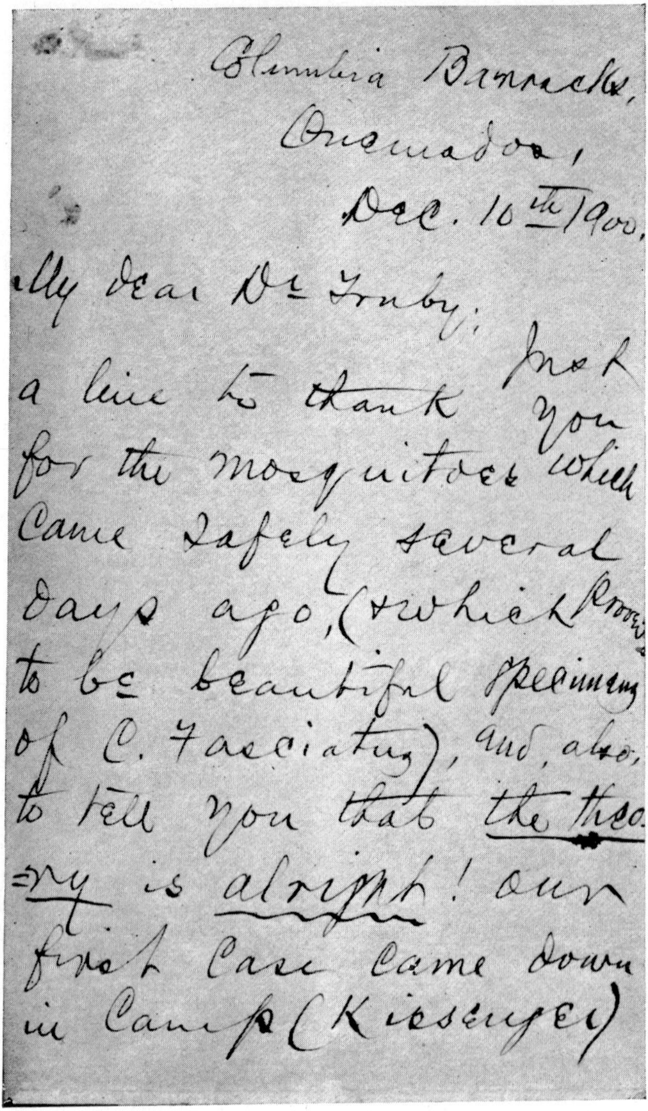

Columbia Barracks,
Quemados,
Dec. 10th 1900,

My dear Dr Truby:

Just a line to thank you for the mosquitoes which came safely several days ago, (& which prove to be beautiful specimens of C. Fasciatus), and, also, to tell you that the theory is alright! our first case came down in camp (Kissinger)

FIGURE 26

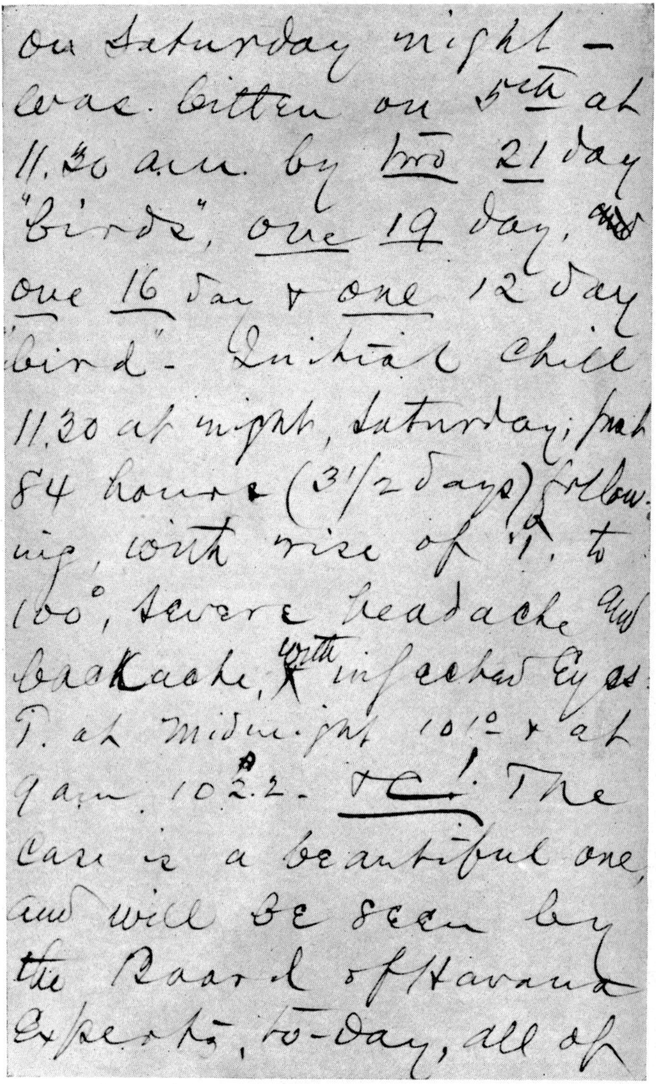

on Saturday night —
was bitten on 5th at
11.30 a.m. by two 21 day
"birds", one 19 day,
one 16 day & one 12 day
"bird". Initial chill
11.30 at night, Saturday; had
84 hours (3½ days) following, with rise of T. to
100°, severe headache and
backache, with infected eyes.
T. at midnight 101° & at
9 a.m. 102.2. &c.! The
case is a beautiful one,
and will be seen by
the Board of Havana
Experts, to-day, all of

FIGURE 26

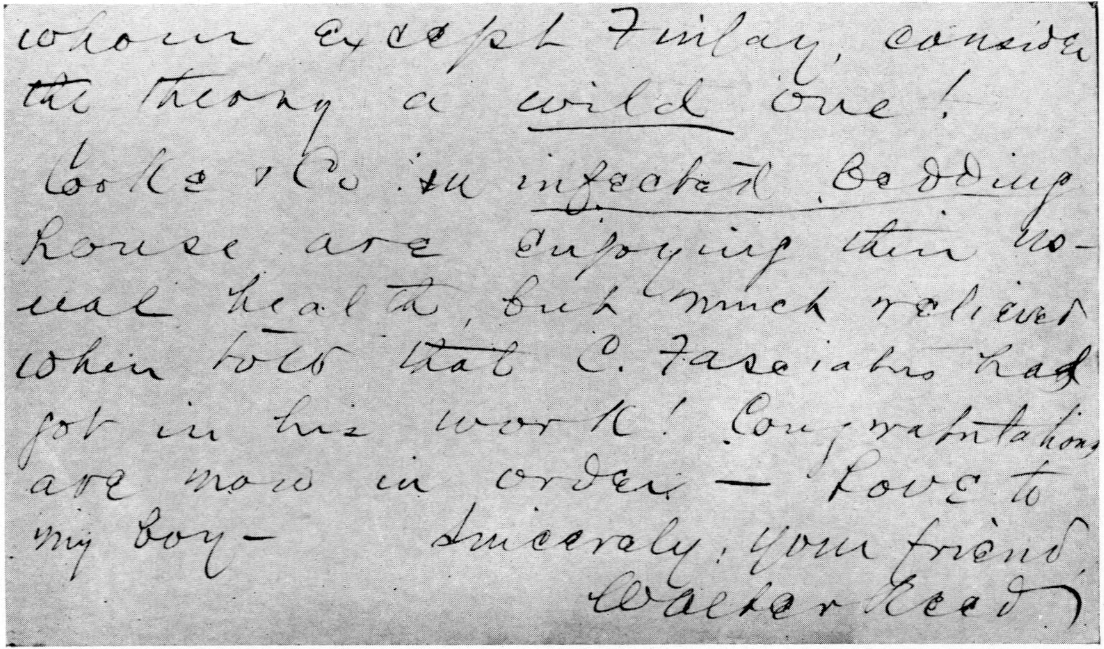
whom except Finlay, consider
the theory a <u>wild</u> one!
Cooke & Co. in <u>infected Bedding</u>
house are enjoying their us-
ual health, but much relieved
when told that C. Fasciatus had
got in his work! Congratulations
are now in order — Love to
my boy — Sincerely, your friend
Walter Reed

FIGURE 26

to the sea. There were more mosquitoes (especially *A. aegypti*) in Cienfuegos than I had ever seen anywhere in Cuba, and they were plentiful enough too at the post as no mosquito control work had been done.

It was not difficult therefore to collect mosquitoes. On December 3, I dispatched a supply of "beautiful" specimens, all *A. aegypti*, to Major Reed with a note describing the situation as just explained, i.e., that the local conditions were not alarming; that the mosquito menace at the post could easily be corrected and that Lawrence was well and happy. In about a week, I received the letter reproduced in Figure 26 in reply.

For over thirty-five years this precious letter had been in a packing box with other letters, papers, pamphlets, and photographs bearing on my experiences in Cuba. While I knew that I had the letter, I did not fully realize its historical significance until, after retirement from active service, time permitted of sorting out of these papers and a study of the important ones. The letter has been presented to the Army Medical Library (long known as the Surgeon General's Library) in Washington, D. C. Surgeon General C. R. Reynolds, in 1938, in writing about this great library, had this to say of the letter:

The library has a very rich collection of American manuscripts, not the least important of which is the newest addition, the original of the letter written by Dr. Walter Reed December 10, 1900, to his friend, Dr. A. E. Truby, of the Army, in which he calmly announces the success of his yellow fever experiment in Cuba. His first case had come down with the disease, Private Kissinger (still alive). "The case is a beautiful one," Reed wrote, "and will be seen by the Board of Havana experts today, all of whom, except Finlay, consider the theory a wild one!" On that board was the noted Surgeon General William C. Gorgas.

It is interesting to note that this pen letter of Walter Reed's is probably the earliest written account of the first experimental case (Kissinger) at Camp Lazear. The description of the case is almost identical with the wording given in the published report of the Board two months later. A careful study of the letter shows how keenly happy and excited he was so early on the morning of December 10. The evening before, he had written a letter to his wife in Washington announcing his success and explaining the importance of the discovery. The two letters supplement each other in showing his enthusiasm and great joy. I doubt if he slept much that night for in the letter to Mrs. Reed, it is clear that he made a very late visit to see Kissinger and he must have been up at daylight to write my letter, have his breakfast and then, on his way to Camp Lazear, drop his outgoing mail (Mrs.

Reed's letter and mine) at the Marianao Post Office.
Mine was postmarked at 8 A.M. December 10, 1900.
Walter Reed's letter to his wife.[24]

COLUMBIA BARRACKS, QUEMADOS, CUBA
Dec. 9, 1900

It is with a great deal of pleasure that I hasten to tell
you that we have succeeded in producing a case of unmistakable yellow fever by the bite of the mosquito.
Our first case in the experimental camp developed at
11:30 last night, commencing with a sudden chill followed by fever. He had been bitten at 11:30 * December
5th, and hence his attack followed just three and a half
days after the bite. As he had been in our camp 15 days
before being inoculated and had had no other possible ex-
posure, the case is as clear as the sun at noon-day, and
sustains brilliantly and conclusively our conclusions.
Thus, just 18 days from the time we began our experimental work we have succeeded in demonstrating this
mode of propagation of the disease, so that the most
doubtful and sceptical must yield. Rejoice with me,
sweetheart, as, aside from the antitoxin of diphtheria and
Koch's discovery of the tubercle bacillus, it will be re-
garded as the most important piece of work, scientifically,
during the 19th century. I do not exaggerate, and I

[24] Howard A. Kelly: Walter Reed and Yellow Fever. Ed. 1,
p. 140.
 * Probably a *lapsus pennae* for 2:30, which is the time stated
in the published record.

could shout for very joy that heaven has permitted me to establish this wonderful way of propagating yellow fever. It was Finlay's theory, and he deserves great credit for having suggested it, but as he did nothing to prove it, it was rejected by all, including General Sternberg. Now we have put it beyond cavil, and its importance to Cuba and the United States cannot be estimated. Major Kean says that the discovery is worth more than the cost of the Spanish War, including lives lost and money expended. He is almost beside himself with joy and will tell General Wood when he goes to town in the morning. Tomorrow afternoon we will have the Havana Board of Experts, Drs. Guiteras, Albertini, and Finlay, come out and diagnose the case. I shan't tell them how the infection was acquired until after they have satisfied themselves concerning the character of the case, then I will let them know. I suppose that old Dr. Finlay will be delighted beyond bounds, as he will see his theory at last fully vindicated. 9:30 P.M. Since writing the above our patient has been doing well. His temperature, which was 102.5° at noon, has fallen to 101° and his severe headache and backache have subsided considerably. Everything points, as far as it can at this stage, to a favourable termination, for which I feel so happy.

The "Board of Havana Experts" consisted of Drs. Juan Guiteras, Carlos Finlay, A. Diaz Albertini, and Major W. C. Gorgas. All of them were very com-

petent doctors who were without doubt as expert in
the diagnosis of yellow fever as any group of medical
men in the world. Dr. Guiteras was the professor of
pathology at the Medical School of the University of
Pennsylvania while I was a student there. The long
experience of these men had taught them to be cautious in adopting new ideas and theories, especially in
this disease the etiology of which had been attributed
from time to time to almost everything. Nothing had
ever been proved. Every member of the Board (except Finlay) was skeptical and up to this time had
considered the theory "a wild one." Two of them
were Cubans and all of them had long known of
Finlay's theory and of his inability to prove it. Gorgas,
who had known Reed a long time and who was aware
of his reputation as a careful scientific investigator,
was just as skeptical as any of the other members.
Other Cuban experts also came to examine the first
four experimental cases, among them Drs. Bango,
Sanches, and Moas, and they all confirmed the diagnosis. The Board had seen Kissinger on December
10 at which time they did not make a positive diagnosis although Ames had no doubts about it at that
time. On December 11, one of the members pronounced it yellow fever and all concurred in the
diagnosis later.

My personal observations on the work at Camp Lazear of course came to an end on October 30 but from the official reports and Reed's letters, it is quite evident that there was little change in the set-up, personnel, equipment, or in the routine work at the camp.

The following letters from Walter Reed to General Sternberg first appeared in the "Biography of George Miller Sternberg" written by his wife, Martha C. Sternberg, and published in 1920 by the American Medical Association. They have been reproduced by permission of the Association through its secretary, Dr. Morris Fishbein. These letters furnish very important details not found in the official reports. They have been most helpful to me in my efforts to get all the facts together. With a clear picture of the scene and the personnel still before me, it is believed that the comments on these letters may help to clear up certain details not generally understood.

Major Reed to General Sternberg:

December 14, 1900

Within three weeks of the establishment of our experimental station, I am able to report two cases of yellow fever brought about by the bites of infected mosquitoes— one occurring suddenly at 11:30 P.M., December 8, and the second 9:30 P.M. December 12. Both cases have been seen and carefully examined by the board of experts, consisting of Drs. Guiteras, Finlay, Gorgas and Albertini, and both have been pronounced to be unmistakable cases of yellow fever. I thought it best to have these gentlemen of acknowledged experience see all of our cases. This they have gladly done, visiting our first case on the 9th, 11th and again today. Although our second case is only in his second day, the symptoms are unmistakable. A third case bitten on the 11th at 4:30 P.M. began to sicken yesterday afternoon, with some fever and headache, and has, today, developed a temperature of 100.8°. I think that he will be removed early tomorrow morning, as his symptoms point plainly in that direction. Concerning a fourth case, bitten three days ago, it is as yet too early to pronounce an opinion. Our three non-immunes have already passed fourteen nights in a house horribly infected with clothing and bedding without showing any symptoms whatever. Perhaps it is as yet too early to pronounce an opinion as to the probability of their escape. Taken altogether, we feel very much pleased with our results, and believe that, with your kind permission, we should present a supplementary note to the Pan-American Congress in February next.

I am glad that our first case, now in his sixth day, is doing very well. It is too early to give a prognosis in our second case. In view of these results, I would like to know whether you consider it necessary that we should try blood injections, as you suggested when I last saw you. Any other suggestions that you may make will be much appreciated.

Major Reed to General Sternberg:

December 16, 1900

I cabled you again today as I thought that you would be pleased to hear that success was still attending our efforts. Our fourth case sickened yesterday afternoon at 2:30 o'clock, and at 9 P.M. had a temperature of 104.2°. Four cases out of five inoculations is quite satisfactory, we think. This morning Doctors Guiteras, Finlay and Albertini were again here to see our third and fourth cases. Like the first two, the diagnosis was very plain and hence they very promptly pronounced the cases to be yellow fever, our first three we consider out of danger. The last man is still quite sick. Our third case was a very mild one. Although coming down four and one-half hours within the usual period of incubation— five days—he could have passed quarantine on the morning of his sixth day, and would have been the focus of one of those epidemics ascribed to infected bedding, or the unpacking of trunk. For this reason, it is, to me, the most interesting case of the series. This week I hope to loose infected mosquitoes in our building No. 2, my intention being to demonstrate conclusively how a building becomes infected. Of course, every precaution has been taken to prevent the escape of these insects. My control subjects will keep on the uninfected side of the building, being protected by a fine wire-screen partition but breathing the same atmosphere. I have to ask as a special favor that Acting Assistant Surgeon R. P. Cooke, who so courageously volunteered to take charge of affairs in our horribly infected clothing building No. 1, may not have his contract annulled, but may be sent to duty in the Philippines, if he cannot remain in Cuba. His interest in the work deserves, I think, this consideration from the Department.

The search for the parasite will be next in order.

No results were obtained during the first two weeks due, as Reed thought, to the cold weather which retarded the development of the "parasite" (now known to be a virus) in the mosquito. During that period Kissinger and Moran had both been bitten, without results, by mosquitoes that had bitten severe cases from eleven to fourteen days before. In the third week, with warmer weather and older mosquitoes, four of the five cases bitten (Kissinger and three Spaniards) developed the disease. Moran, bitten on November 29 by a fifteen-day mosquito, remained perfectly well. From December 15 until December 25, no cases developed in camp since no volunteers were bitten. This hiatus in the experimental work definitely showed that the camp was not infected. The "Additional Note" stated: "The epidemic having ceased on December 15, 1900, no other cases of yellow fever occurred in the camp until we again began

to expose individuals to inoculation." [25] On December
21, the new experiment to demonstrate how a house
becomes infected was started when Moran entered
the "infected mosquito building." The request in the
letter of December 14 for advice about trying the
blood injections proposed by General Sternberg indicates, I think, that Reed was not very keen to subject
men to this risk. He was now positive that the mosquito theory was sound and that by February, he
would be able to submit a report that would convince
everyone else to that effect.

Major Reed to General Sternberg:

December 22, 1900

I write to request that Dr. McConnell, of the Museum,
may be sent down to join us on the next transport leaving New York. I would like to have him make drawings
of the mosquito and larvae from live specimens. There
is some other work here which he could also do. He
should bring camera lucida and suitable paper for doing
this work.

I would like also to be made a delegate to the Pan-
American Congress, if you approve of our presenting a
supplementary note at this meeting.

Some of the sketches made by Dr. McConnell at
that time may be seen in the article by Reed and

[25] The Etiology of Yellow Fever—An Additional Note. Senate
Document No. 822, 1911, p. 80.

Carroll on "The Prevention of Yellow Fever" published in 1900.[26]

The president of the Board was now, at the close of the year and the end of the century, ready to tell the world at the Pan-American Congress how yellow fever was transmitted. His letter to his wife in the closing minutes of the old century beautifully expressed his sentiments at that moment:

COLUMBIA BARRACKS,
QUEMADOS, CUBA
11:50 P.M. Dec. 31, 1900

Only ten minutes of the old century remain. Here I have been sitting, reading that most wonderful book, "La Roche on Yellow Fever" written in 1853. Forty-seven years later it has been permitted to me and my assistants to lift the impenetrable veil that has surrounded the causation of this most wonderful, dreadful pest of humanity and to put it on a rational and scientific basis. I thank God that this has been accomplished during the latter days of the old century. May its cure be wrought in the early days of the new! The prayer that has been mine for twenty years, that I might be permitted to do something to alleviate human suffering has been granted! . . . Hark, there go the twenty-four buglers in concert, all sounding "taps" for the old year.[27]

[26] Senate Document, No. 822, 61st Congress, 1911, pp. 136–137.
[27] Howard A. Kelly: Walter Reed and Yellow Fever. Ed. 1, p. 152.

Major Reed to General Sternberg:

January 1, 1901

I am in receipt of your letter informing me that I would be detailed as a delegate to the Pan-American Congress, and thank you for the same. I am sure that you will be interested to know that our attempt to infect a new building by means of contaminated mosquitoes has met with complete success. The insects were released in this building during the afternoon of December 21. A few minutes thereafter I permitted a non-immune to enter and lie on a bed provided for the purpose. I, with other nonimmunes, stood in one end of the room, protected, of course, by a wire screen partition. The subject remained 30 minutes and was bitten by several insects. He again entered at 4 P.M. and remained 15 minutes; and again the next afternoon (22d) remaining 15 minutes. During each of which times, he was bitten by one or more insects. Four days later (December 25), at 9 A.M., he felt badly and had fever 99.6. At noon, a slight chill with rising temperature, 100.4—backache, headache, suffused face and injected eyes—at 9 P.M., temperature 104.2 —albumen on second evening, jaundice of eyes, etc.— typical symptoms of yellow fever, the diagnosis being confirmed by board of experts. His temperature fell to normal yesterday, sixth day, and patient will make a good recovery. It is hardly necessary to add that the two non-immunes who have slept each night in a noninfected end of the same room, only protected by a wire screen partition, are still well and healthy. Nothing could possibly be more striking than this observation. We shall make but few more experiments—one blood injection has given no result—we will make two others, if I can find the cases. I consider it now very important to find if possible the parasite in the body of the mosquito. We have preserved a number of insects of various ages for paraffin sectioning, when we return to Washington. I will, therefore, thank you very much if you will have the necessary order issued relieving us from duty at this post and authorizing our return to our proper station, so that we can start back immediately after the adjournment of the Pan-American Congress. I will request General Wood to retain the buildings at our camp site, so that, if necessary, we could resume our observations when the epidemic year begins again. Dr. Cooke's services at the Camp are now no longer needed. With greetings of the New Year,

WALTER REED

P. S. No results as yet in infected clothing building. Non-immunes sleeping every night in yellow fever beds.

The January 1 letter is most interesting since it tells how he and other non-immunes watched through the screening, while Moran was being bitten by the free mosquitoes. Two of these non-immunes slept on the screen-protected side of the building from December 21 to January 8 and remained well. The of-

ficial report states that "only one of these insects, a
24-day mosquito, was considered capable of carrying
the infection."

Reed now was apparently anxious to get back to
his laboratory in Washington where an intensive
study could be made on the insects with a view to
finding the "parasite." Carroll had been futilely working at that in addition to his other duties. He began
this study before he went north on sick leave and
was obsessed with the idea that he could find a parasite similar to the one found in malaria. At that time,
however, he was still too ill to do any careful work
at the laboratory but he tried hard. By January 1 the
Board felt that but few more experiments were necessary. Two more blood injection tests were to be made,
no doubt upon instructions from the Surgeon General.
At this time it seems quite probable that Reed had
been persuaded by his friends that it would be fool-
hardy to submit himself to the test, and he was ready
to end the work in Cuba. He himself knew that it
was, but the moral obligation still bothered him. Camp
Lazear was leased by the month and the rental for the
site was continued for several months upon Reed's
request after the experimental work there was discontinued. The prompt results in controlling yellow
fever in Havana during the summer months of 1901
then led to the discontinuance of the lease as further

tests were not necessary. The request made in the letter of December 16 resulted in Dr. Cooke's retention in service and he remained at Camp Columbia until some time after the experiments of the Board were finished.

Major Reed to General Sternberg:

January 13, 1901

Your letter of January 8 was received yesterday. I have made Carroll acquainted with the contents of your letter and he wishes me to convey to you his sincere thanks for the honor which you propose to confer upon him. He will gladly remain in Cuba for a while, as you suggest. It occurs to me that the passage of the Army Bill will promptly promote Major Kean to a majority in the regular Corps, and leave a vacancy for Carroll's promotion. If, however, the new Army Bill limits Surgeons of Volunteers to those who serve in the Philippines, Carroll would not care to go there. If it could be so arranged that he could return to Washington by April 1, I would be much gratified. I would suggest that the order for my own return and Steward Neate's be issued soon, that we could get our outfit on the transport ahead of us, and thus not be compelled to wait several weeks for important material. We could then leave immediately after the adjournment of the Pan-American Congress.

I feel certain that you will be much interested in the result of our blood injections. I think that I mentioned, in a letter, one case that had received a blood injection made on the first day of the disease. The result was negative in this case, unless we regard slight headache and general muscular soreness, on the eighth and ninth days, as some manifestations of an attempt at infection. It is interesting to note that this same individual has since resisted the bite of mosquitoes that conveyed a good typical case of yellow fever to another non-immune. I am inclined, therefore, in the light of other injections, to look upon him as one having a natural immunity to the disease. Having succeeded in getting hold of two hospital corps men, who were willing to take blood injections, we first infected a Spaniard by the bite of mosquitoes. During his primary paroxysms (first day) we injected 2. c.c. of blood from a vein at the elbow subcutaneously in one of our subjects. In just four days, lacking two hours, he developed an attack of yellow fever. From his vein, at the end of twelve hours (temperature 103.4°) we took 1.5 c.c. of blood and injected subcutaneously into second subject, resulting in a pretty infection in two days, twelve hours. Much to my regret we had no one for another injection. The parasite is therefore in the general circulation, and yellow fever thus follows exactly the modes of conveyance found in malarial fever. I have already saturated towels with blood of these cases and have put them in our infected clothing house. Probably nothing will come of this attempt to convey infection. We now have six successes out of seven attempted by means of mosquito bites (85.71 per cent). McConnell is here at work.

Major Reed was always interested in Carroll's welfare and his remarks in the second paragraph resulted in Carroll being made a Major of Volunteers and allowed to continue his duties in Cuba and the United States as Reed's assistant. Attention is directed to the interesting remarks in this and the preceding letter regarding the blood injections. The failure of positive results in the first case (Alvarez, a Spanish volunteer) may have been due to an acquired immunity since it was never possible to determine positively where the men had lived before their recent arrival in Havana. Their own statements could not always be relied upon. It now seems that the slight symptoms on the eighth and ninth days probably constituted a mild, atypical attack which immunized him. The *neutralization* test is now available to definitely determine such cases.

Private Jernegan was the enlisted man who, on January 4, 1901, received the 2 c.c. of blood from the experimental mosquito-borne case of yellow fever (Martinez). Private Olsen was the second enlisted man and he received 1.5 c.c. of Jernegan's blood. There were no more volunteers for blood injections until January 22 when Private Forbes received 0.5 c.c. of blood from a severe case of yellow fever. Another non-immune member of the Hospital Corps Detachment then volunteered, and as *controls* Kissinger, Moran and two Spaniards, all four being immunes, were selected to receive injections of Forbes' blood. At the last moment, however, the non-immune changed his mind and Reed, much perturbed, suddenly announced to Carroll at the laboratory that he would himself take the place of the non-immune. Evidently the pledge made by the members of the Board, although every fair-minded person would agree that circumstances had cancelled that obligation as far as Reed was concerned, again arose to bother him. Carroll protested most vigorously according to J. H. Andrus who overheard the entire conversation while on duty there at that time as a private in the Hospital Corps.

The next morning, January 25, Reed came to the laboratory still determined to take the test and at that point Andrus came forward and volunteered. After some discussion and a full explanation of the dangers, Andrus * took an injection of 1 c.c. of Forbes' blood at 12:15 P.M. on January 25, 1901. On the afternoon of January 28, he was definitely ill and a severe case of yellow fever developed. "The four *controls* were also injected, sub-cutaneously, with 1 c.c. of the same blood without manifesting any symptoms whatever."

Major Reed to General Sternberg:

* Mr. John H. Andrus made his home at Camden, N. J., and died May 1, 1942.

January 27, 1901

As McConnell has completed his drawings here, I have concluded to let him go on transport *Rawlins* which leaves today instead of waiting for the next boat. He carries with him a copy of our additional note with charts. I hope that Dr. Gould this time will return proofs to you so that corrections can be made before final publication. The article would be in time, if it appeared about February 10–15. I trust that what I have written may meet with your approval. I hope to leave here on Ward Line steamer leaving Havana, February 9. Have no order yet for Neate's relief from this station, but trust that it will come soon as well as order relieving *Private Andrus* and assigning him to Army Medical School laboratory. I will ask you to make a slight change in the wording of our eighth conclusion, so that the word "contaminated" be inserted before the word mosquitoes—so that it will read as follows: "A house may be said to be infected with yellow fever only when there are present within its walls contaminated mosquitoes capable of conveying the parasite of this disease." I will, also, ask that you change the relative position of conclusions No. 9 and 10, so that No. 9 will come last.

Andrus, who had been working in the laboratory for the past four months, had evidently done exceptionally well; otherwise there would have been no reason to take him to Washington where well-qualified men could always be obtained. Two days before,

Andrus had taken a blood injection and on the next day (January 28) developed a severe case of yellow fever. A carbuncle in the sacral region greatly retarded his recovery and he was not physically able to return to the States at the time Reed left. His enlistment expired on April 25 and he returned to his home.

Major Reed to General Sternberg:

January 31, 1901

I cabled to you this afternoon, requesting that you delay publication of our additional note until you receive the copy which I shall mail in the morning. I have inserted a *footnote* of importance which I thought should accompany the note when published. Although our immune (mosquito made) cases, four in number, have shown no symptoms whatever, I am very uneasy about the nonimmune soldier * who got the same quantity of blood (1 c.c.) at the same time. He seems to have acquired a very serious infection, his temperature running along the 104° line now for three days. Albumen appeared at the end of eighteen hours, but it is not excessive. Should he die, I shall regret that I ever undertook this work. The responsibility for the life of a human being weighs upon me very heavily just at present, and I am dreadfully melancholic. Everything is being done for him that we know how to do. This after-

* Private John H. Andrus.

noon the Mexican delegates were here to see our cases and afterwards visited the experimental camp. They seemed to be wonderfully impressed with what they heard and saw. Please substitute the copy which I shall forward tomorrow for the copy McConnell brought. I will ask that McConnell change the period of incubation on chart No. 11 to five days, seventeen hours. Although the patient took to bed, complaining of headache, etc. at the end of four days, twenty hours, his febrile paroxysm did not begin till five days and seventeen hours. If you think that the disease begins with the advent of premonitory symptoms, you can let it stand as at present. I leave that to you entirely. I shall hope to leave on the *McPherson* about February 8.

Sincerely yours,
WALTER REED

The "footnote"[28] referred to the case of Andrus and the four controls. This experiment evidently took place after the report had been completed. The non-immune soldier whom Reed was so worried about was Private Andrus.

It will be remembered that the "Preliminary Note" was written under rather hectic conditions. The preparation of the second report, "An Additional Note," was a much simpler matter. The events in each case were no doubt recorded from day to day;

[28] The Etiology of Yellow Fever—An Additional Note. Senate Document No. 822, 1911, p. 82 (footnote).

all members of the Board were present to help and there was no necessity to search for unrecorded details, many of which were carried to the grave by a deceased member in the first instance. In less than two months from the day the first case was taken sick at Camp Lazear, the Board's report entitled "The Etiology of Yellow Fever—An Additional Note" was read by Reed at the Pan-American Medical Congress in Havana, Cuba, on February 6, 1901. This report definitely proved the statement that "the theory is all right." The thoroughness of the experiments done in such a short period of time, and without the death of a single case, amazed the scientific world; the conclusions drawn have stood the test of time, although supplemented by additional information gained by years of splendid work by other scientific men, especially those of the Rockefeller Foundation working in New York, Africa, and South America.

CHAPTER TWELVE

CREDIT FOR THE GREAT ACHIEVEMENT

TO Dr. Carlos J. Finlay of Havana goes the credit for having conceived the idea of the rôle of the mosquito in yellow fever; to Walter Reed and his associates, Carroll, Agramonte, and Lazear, goes the credit for demonstrating that rôle. In the words of the late Dr. Joseph Goldwater of the Public Health Service, Reed "converted a discredited hypothesis into an established doctrine."

From Walter Reed's published reports and statements, it is quite evident that he desired that all members of the Board should share equally in the credit for the work. There was no indication that he claimed or desired any particular credit for himself. The members, working together on a duly constituted board of the Army, achieved the goal set for them, and to them belongs all the credit for the great achievement. In this detailed account of my observations in Cuba and my interpretations of the events, Walter Reed naturally occupies the center of the picture. He, as president, organized the Board and directed its work in accordance with the provisions of Army Regulations and the customs of the service. His long Army experience, temperament, analytical mind, and scientific training made him especially well fitted for leadership in work of this kind. The medical profession, indeed the whole world, knows this and Walter Reed is secure in his fame. Anything that I could say would not add to the greatness of his work. The same statement applies to Dr. Lazear, the martyr to science, and to Carroll and Agramonte who performed the duties assigned them to the satisfaction of their leader. They were all skilled in their specialties. There were, as many know, most unfortunate controversies after Reed's death as to who did this or that but they can best be forgotten as they had nothing to do with the results obtained. They would never have occurred if Reed had lived a few years longer. Each member of the Board admired and respected Reed, and recognized his great qualification for the work in hand.

From a broader viewpoint, this was an Army Medical Department achievement. All of the active participants, including most of the volunteers for the tests, were serving in that Department. Among them were officers (including contract surgeons) from the Surgeon General down to and including privates of the Hospital Corps. Each one aided in bringing about a solution to the baffling mystery. In many instances, the parts played were heroic. It is felt that a brief review of those who gave the Board valuable advice and material aid may be of interest.

The Surgeon General. Much credit belongs to Brigadier General George M. Sternberg for his part in organizing and directing the work of the board. He had devoted many years to the study of yellow fever and had been able to disprove every bacteriological theory concerning its etiology until Sanarelli published his claims in 1897. He therefore had Reed investigate that theory at the laboratory of the Army Medical School in Washington. While this work was going on in 1899, he sent Reed to Cuba on several investigating expeditions. The laboratory work in Washington had convinced Reed that *B. icteroides* was not the specific organism involved. His trip to Havana, where the Marine Hospital Commission was studying the same organism, convinced him that he should also make studies in Havana where blood cultures from incipient cases of yellow fever could be obtained. About the middle of May 1900, Sternberg and Reed had a conference and at that time they planned the campaign and selected the members of the Board. On May 23, the Surgeon General requested the necessary orders. General Sternberg gave the board every possible assistance and was in constant communication with its president.

The Governor General of Cuba. Major General Leonard Wood, U. S. V., was a close friend of Walter Reed. Both were members of the Medical Department, Wood being a captain in the regular establishment. As Governor General, he naturally was intensely interested in the control of yellow fever and he had the authority to give unlimited assistance to the Board. Being a medical man himself, he readily appreciated the problem as outlined by Reed. He gave his full support and was deeply interested in the work. When the question of testing the mosquito theory on human subjects arose, he at once approved the idea and told Reed to go ahead. Who else in high office could or would have granted such a procedure? Without his support, there would have been no way at that time of proving the mosquito theory, as it was not then known that a certain species of monkey was susceptible to yellow fever. Wood provided funds for the camp and for gratuities; arranged for volunteers with the Spanish Consul; in fact, authorized everything that was asked for. The Board, in its second report, "An Additional Note," acknowledged this indebtedness, in the following words:

We desire to here express our sincere thanks to the Military Governor of the Island of Cuba, Major General Leonard Wood, United States Volunteers, without whose approval and assistance these observations could not have been carried out.

Later on, when it became known that the mosquito transmitted yellow fever, General Wood became just as energetic in the work of eradicating the disease from Havana. He immediately got behind his Chief Sanitary Officer, Gorgas, gave him *carte blanche* authority and ample funds. Very little has been told of the importance of his activities regarding this work.

The Chief Surgeon, Division of Cuba. Major Valery Havard was a loyal supporter of Reed's, and was always glad to assist in the work but since his chief, General Wood, was taking such an active part, he had little opportunity to help. When the Board's report incriminating the mosquito was published, Havard's office was the first to prepare and issue instructions to all medical officers in Cuba on mosquito control and other measures required by the new discovery to successfully fight the spread of this disease. For the first time in history, medical officers were told that:

As it has been demonstrated that yellow fever cannot be conveyed by fomites, such as bedding, clothing, effects, and baggage, *they need not be subjected to any special disinfection.* Care should be taken, however, not to remove them from the infected rooms until after formaldehyde fumigation, so that they may not harbor infected mosquitoes.

Publication was delayed to obtain the sanction of the Surgeon General but the order was issued on April 27, 1901, as Circular No. 5, Headquarters Department of Cuba (Appendix VII). In the city of Havana, the part of the order eliminating disinfection was disregarded, as Gorgas was still not convinced that the mosquito was the *only way* of transmitting yellow fever.

The Chief Sanitary Officer of Havana. Major William C. Gorgas and Reed were also old friends and they frequently discussed the yellow fever problem in Cuba. Outside of that, Gorgas took no part in the work and was not optimistic about the prospects of the Board in getting any real results. He was also a friend of Finlay's, admired his work and knowledge of yellow fever and, because Finlay after years of experimenting with infected *A. aegypti* could not prove his mosquito theory, he probably felt that no one else could. When cases developed at Camp Lazear, Gorgas (as a member of the Havana board of yellow fever experts) came to see them and always confirmed the diagnosis. Not until then did he become convinced that the mosquito could transmit yellow fever.

Gorgas, in his 1902 report as Chief Sanitary Officer of Havana, commented as follows on the Board's findings:

The idea was so new and so entirely contrary to all former theories on the subject and apparently to all former experience, that the paper was received with scant belief. I myself had seen the work and was convinced that the mosquito could convey yellow fever but I was hardly prepared to believe that it was the only way or even the ordinary way of conveying the disease.

In the same report, he states:

I had very little hope of accomplishing much. It seemed to me that even if the mosquito did convey yellow fever, he could not be gotten rid of but as he evidently could carry the disease, it was our duty to take precautions in that direction.

He seems to have been slow in getting into action on mosquito control work but sometime in March 1901, with characteristic thoroughness he organized mosquito brigades, and required that all fever cases in Havana be most carefully screened from mosquitoes. However, he continued the routine disinfection of everything until August 15, 1901, as previously related. Gorgas was not finally convinced that the mosquito was the principal means of conveying yellow fever until, in his own campaign in Havana against mosquitoes, he obtained such immediate and startling results. There were nine deaths in Havana from yellow fever in January 1901. There were five deaths in February. Mosquito extermination and screening of yellow fever cases began in March, and there was one death that month. There were none in April, May, or June; one in July; two in August; two in September; and none in the following nine months. This in Havana where yellow fever had been constantly present for one hundred and fifty years! Coming so promptly after the announcement of the Board's findings, these striking results constituted a great practical demonstration which astounded the world. It brought well-earned fame to Major Gorgas whose outstanding administrative ability, tenacity of purpose, and attention to details were responsible for the wonderful results.

The Chief Surgeon, Department of Havana, and Pinar del Rio. Major Jefferson Randolph Kean, U. S. V. (Captain, U. S. A.), was another close friend of Reed's who was untiring in his efforts to assist him in every possible way. With his authority as Chief Surgeon of the Department, he gave us personal instructions which resulted in placing the ideal facilities of the post hospital at Reed's disposal. All of the assistance given the Board by members of the detachment, as well as the supplies furnished by the hospital, were based entirely on such verbal instructions. No official orders were issued covering the duties of the doctors or enlisted men at Camp Lazear. Complete harmony and a spirit of co-operation existed throughout and post Headquarters never interfered, being satisfied with the informality of our arrangements. Reed undoubtedly depended more on Kean's advice than on that of anyone else in Cuba. Kean was the first officer to start an antimosquito campaign. He was energetic, always on the job, handled his department with tact and efficiency, and had the confidence of his chief, General Fitzhugh Lee.

Kean, in addition to his other duties, was Acting Chief Surgeon, Department of Cuba, from November 19 to January 8, 1901, while Colonel Havard was on leave. Why he was selected for this duty instead of Gorgas the senior, who was in Havana, I do not know. While occupying that position, Kean wrote General Order No. 6 (Appendix VI). This epoch-making order directed mosquito control work at *all* military posts in Cuba, but it did not apply to the city of Havana. Reed in a letter to Dr. L. O. Howard, Chief of the Bureau of Entomology in Washington, wrote (January 13, 1901):

Major J. R. Kean, Surgeon U. S. A., was the Acting Chief Surgeon, Division of Cuba at the time this order was published, and it was he who drew it up and recommended it to General Wood. He should have credit for it.

It is pleasing to be able to record the facts here.

Next to General Wood, I am certain that Kean did more than anyone else in Cuba toward making the Board's work successful. After Reed's death, members of Congress frequently asked the Surgeon General for information about the Board's work. It was Kean who usually wrote the answers. On several occasions, when I was in Washington, my views were obtained. The Surgeon General's office has always done its utmost to keep the records of these historical achievements clean and straight. The brunt of this work fell to Surgeon General M. W. Ireland who, with Kean's help, did the work conscientiously and exceedingly well.

All of the officers mentioned, except Surgeon General Sternberg, were serving in Havana or the vicinity (1900), and it is of interest in connection with their service to Reed to show their relative rank and ages. Havard, Reed, and Gorgas were the seniors, ranking as majors in the regular establishment. Kean and Wood were captains, ranking in the order named. Their ages and the dates of their first commission in the Army are given below:

RANK IN MEDICAL CORPS OF REGULAR ARMY	DATE OF BIRTH	DATE OF FIRST COMMISSION IN MEDICAL DEPARTMENT OF ARMY
Major Valery Havard	1846	1874
Major Walter Reed	1850	1875
Major W. C. Gorgas	1854	1880
Captain J. R. Kean	1860	1884
Captain Leonard Wood	1860	1886

Kean at the time (1900) also held the temporary rank of Major in the Volunteer Army. Wood, the junior of the group, was a Captain in the Regular Service. In the early spring of 1898, Lieutenant Colonel Theodore Roosevelt, U. S. Volunteers, organized the "Rough Rider" regiment and selected his friend, Captain Leonard Wood, to command it as a Colonel of Volunteers. In July of the same year, he was promoted to Brigadier General, U. S. Volunteers, and in December to Major General, U. S. Volunteers. On February 4, 1901, he was made a Brigadier General in the Regular Army and then ceased to be an officer in the Medical Department. Soon after this, he became a Major General, U. S. Army.

The Staff of the Hospital at Columbia Barracks. Captain Alexander N. Stark was another of the loyal friends who gave Reed most cordial support and assistance. Reed was especially fond of Stark. The latter was full of wit and humor and was known throughout the service for the almost endless number of marvelous stories he had ready for every occasion. Reed, although more serious-minded, enjoyed them immensely, for he too had a keen sense of humor. Stark left for the United States on September 3 while Lazear was in the midst of his experiments with mosquitoes.

The other members of the staff, Drs. Lazear, Pinto, Ames, De Poorter, Amador, and Truby were always ready and available to assist in any way possible. Likewise the loyalty, companionship, and good fellowship of this group added much to the comfort of Reed and Carroll while they lived in our quarters and shared our mess. The facilities of the hospital proved to be of great value to the Board. Quarters, messing facilities, supplies, equipment, transportation, trained enlisted personnel, nurses and a yellow fever hospital, with an expert in charge, meant much to Reed. Possibly the loss of one or two patients in the early work at Camp Lazear would have stopped all further "guinea pig" tests. I am sure that Reed realized such a possibility and that the extent of the investigations depended very greatly on the ability of Dr. Roger Post Ames. Reed was never happy about this work of endangering human lives and one can imagine how delighted he was at the end to know that not one of his experimental cases had perished. It has always been my opinion that the success of Dr. Ames in the treatment of this disease was due especially to the early care and treatment his patients received. Suspicious cases were, if possible, carried to the hospital on the beds they occupied. In the Camp Lazear cases, the patient's bed (with patient on it) was placed in the ambulance and taken to the yellow fever hospital with a minimum of disturbance to the patient. He was never permitted out of bed and absolute quiet was insisted upon. Divided doses of calomel, followed by magnesium sulphate, were always given promptly on admission. No food was permitted, not even milk during the febrile stage. Thus, before a diagnosis could be made and before the patient was seriously ill, his system was in condition to battle with the virus of this deadly disease. Of the fourteen cases of yellow fever contracted at Camp Lazear by mosquito bites and blood injections, not a single patient was lost. Treatment in every case was started at the very onset of the premonitory symptoms. This was usually twenty-four or even forty-eight hours before a positive diagnosis of yellow fever could be made. Dr. Ames was a loyal and efficient member of the hospital staff, but he performed no hazardous or exceptional duties with the Board which, in my opinion, would entitle his name to be placed on the "Roll of Honor" with the volunteers. Likewise, the other staff members, including the enlisted men, who did not undergo hazardous tests, deserve commendation only for their loyal co-operation.

Enlisted Men of the Hospital Corp. The detachment was naturally a very essential part of Camp Lazear. Reed was pleased with the interest shown by the men and the way they performed their duties. Not a single one had to be reprimanded or punished in any way for neglect of duty or infractions of discipline. They were a selected group and their work was a big factor in the outcome. Finally, the crowning event was the heroic action of twelve of our enlisted men in volunteering for the tests. To Reed, this was the most important of all the developments in the early work. He was not optimistic of receiving the full co-operation of the Spanish volunteers and with the sudden development of the first few cases at the camp, his feeling was confirmed.

In fact several of our good-natured Spanish friends who jokingly compared our mosquitoes to "the little flies that buzzed harmlessly about their tables," suddenly appeared to lose all interest in the progress of science and, forgetting for the moment even their own personal aggrandizement, incontinently severed their connection with Camp Lazear.[29]

Five of the Spaniards, however, took the tests and four of them developed yellow fever (Fernandez, Beningo, Presedo, Martinez).

[29] Walter Reed: Baltimore address, April 1901. Senate Document No. 822, 1911, p. 99.

CHAPTER THIRTEEN

WALTER REED

WALTER REED'S early life, education, army career and work in Cuba have been briefly but very beautifully told by such scholars as McCaw, Kelly, Kean, and others. It is at once apparent, however, that the biographical data published about him is indeed very meager. More information could and should be collected and recorded while it is possible to do so. With this idea in mind, it has been my desire to record my observations of the splendid way he performed his duties, the way he lived and worked in Cuba, and the influence and example he set for the younger men who were associated with him. A few observations not covered in other chapters will therefore be pertinent.*

First of all, I should again refer to Dr. L. O. Howard's pamphlets on mosquito control work and of the interest with which Reed studied them and taught his juniors the practical methods advocated therein. In November 1900, before the tests at Camp Lazear had

* See also Appendix IX.

FIG. 27. The Schuler bust of Walter Reed in the lobby of the Walter Reed Hospital, Washington, D.C. (Army Medical Center photograph.) (See page 231.)

FIG. 28. Frame of mosquito cage, with vestibule, used at Army stations in Cuba to keep mosquitoes away from fever cases. (From official report.)

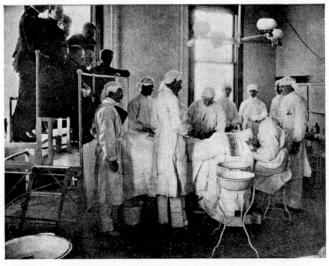

FIG. 29. Operating room, Army General Hospital, Washington, D.C., 1902. *1*, Major W. C. Borden, Medical Corps, conducting a surgical clinic for student officers. *2*, Lieut. J. H. Ford. (From official report.)

started, he was already considering the practical side of the mosquito problem. By the end of the year, the satisfactory results of the oiling campaign at Columbia Barracks were known and at about the same time Kissinger and four other volunteers had developed yellow fever from infected mosquitoes. So on January 13, 1901, Reed wrote Dr. Howard about it. This is an extract from that letter:

The mosquito theory for the propagation of yellow fever is no longer a *theory* but a *well-established fact*. Isn't it enough to make a fellow feel happy? Anopheles and Culex are a gay old pair! What havoc they have wrought on our species during the last three centuries! But with "Howard and kerosene" we are going to knock them out.

When Major Reed came to live at the hospital, he cheerfully conformed to the established routine and seemed to be satisfied with our mode of life, in fact, really to enjoy the experience. While our living conditions were rather crude, we had everything necessary for comfort. Building Number 108, where we all lived, was very well constructed of pine lumber from the States. The floor was from four to five feet above the ground; a ventilating space between the corrugated iron roof and the ceiling leading to three large cowls over the quarters dissipated the heat from the hot roof.

The rafters were 2 by 12 inches and the spaces between them remained open outside of the building and under the porch roof. The ceilings did not go all the way up to the center but a space about 2 feet wide was left open at the top so that the air of the room could pass out through the cowls with the hot air currents under the roof. With the fine ventilation thus obtained and with all doors and windows always open, we had the full benefit of both land and sea breezes. The iron beds and hard cotton mattresses supplied by the Quartermaster were especially suitable for the climate. Folding field chairs and tables were usually a part of every officer's equipment and these were also supplemented by other small articles which each officer wanted for his personal comfort. Food for the officers' mess was purchased from the Army Commissary Department. At that time it was excellent, especially the fresh meats which came direct from the States and which were kept under refrigeration in Havana until the day they were required at the post. The local markets provided us with fresh vegetables and fruits. Our cook at the time was "John Chinaman" who was both faithful and efficient and, best of all, could keep our mess bills down to very reasonable figures. In short, our living conditions were not materially different from those in large Army camps of the present time. Of course we did not have the advantage of electricity for lighting or refrigeration but coal oil lamps and plenty of ice served us exceedingly well. Reed was no stranger to army field conditions and we were really serving under *de luxe* circumstances compared to those of the camps he had recently inspected in the States. I can definitely state that he thoroughly enjoyed his experience at Columbia Barracks.

There was, however, one local condition which Walter Reed did not enjoy, neither did any of the rest of us, although it was the source of much amusement. In the large ventilating spaces between the rafters, a species of tree frogs would collect at certain seasons. They probably came from a large tree (there were only two on the hospital grounds) by the side of Dr. Lazear's quarters and but a few yards from our quarters. As they hopped up the incline of the ceiling in darkness, they often came through the opening at the top and down they would flop with a resounding thud as their heavy, wet bodies struck the floor. Even though that often disturbed sleep, it was not much to complain about. It was quite another thing, however, if they landed on top of the mosquito bar, near your head, and you were awakened by a fine spray on your face as most of us were. One of the doctors, recently arrived, who did not put up a mosquito bar had the experience of having a frog land on his head. From that time on, mosquito bars were always used by everyone and the spraying nuisance avoided by a newspaper or other covering on the bar at the head of the bed. Finally, to cap the climax, you would find all the frogs that had rained down in your quarters during the night in your water pail as you prepared to shave. With the sucking disks on the end of their toes, they would hold themselves to the side of the pail with nothing but their heads out of water. While we had facilities for a good shower bath, our other bathing equipment consisted of a wash basin, a water bucket, and another for waste water. These were cared for by a faithful "striker" employed by the month. Covers were finally obtained for the pails and the frogs found no other stunts to "pull" on us.

One of the nurses has been quoted as saying: "On one occasion, he (Reed) moved his mess quarters because he heard his brother officers using language at the table which was very ungentlemanly."

No such occurrence happened during my service there. I feel quite sure that Reed continued to live and mess with the doctors at Columbia Barracks until his work in Cuba was finished. Although Reed was twenty or more years senior to our group of youngsters, he put up with our pranks and seemed to thoroughly enjoy the experience. On the other hand, if anyone annoyed him, he had a nice way of letting the offender know and there was always a loyal response to his wishes. I feel therefore that any young officer who was guilty of such impropriety would have been disciplined on the spot either by the Major himself or by the Commanding Officer, Captain Stark.

Reed (in 1900) did not seem robust. He was always careful of his diet and ate sparingly. He marvelled at the amount of heavy food, especially meat, the rest of us could get away with. Time after time, I saw him smile and at the same time shake his head and say, "Boys, have mercy on your poor kidneys; they can't be replaced."

We were, however, a young, active group. Our daily duties required real energy; besides, nearly all of us rode horseback, swam, or took part in some athletic sports. Reed and Carroll got little or no exercise when they were busy in their laboratory. At other times, they did a little walking but even that was very limited and consisted mainly of a stroll to Quemados in the early evening. The distance from their quarters to the laboratory, 140 yards, was of course covered several times a day, this really providing the main portion of their daily outdoor exercise. In trips to Havana, transportation was always provided and no one did much walking on the hot streets of Havana. Referring again to Reed's physical condition, it seems quite probable that he was then suffering from chronic appendicitis and that this condition which he did not recognize, was responsible for his being so careful of himself, especially his diet. Appendicitis was the direct cause of his death in 1902.

With the passing of Dr. Lazear, our laboratory was again without a competent bacteriologist. It was then necessary to revert to our old methods of doing the routine laboratory work. The Board's work at the laboratory also came to a standstill as Carroll was sick and Reed was fully occupied writing the "Preliminary Note" and in presenting it to the meeting at Indianapolis. This period from mid-September until Reed's return in November left Steward Neate with little to do except to care for the laboratory cultures and mosquitoes. He aided us greatly in doing the daily urine examinations and such other work as he was competent to perform. Reed not only approved of this but on his return was always ready to assist us in any special cases. He and Carroll both co-operated in every possible way and were always available for consultations in serious medical cases. Atypical cases and obscure tropical diseases were frequently admitted and it meant much to us to have Reed's professional advice and to observe his careful development of the study in each case. I am sure that his methods and example were of lasting benefit to every young doctor present, as they certainly were to me. He was constantly encouraging us to discuss our work with him and likewise he enjoyed inviting discussions about his own work. He had no secrets about his experiments and everyone knew from day to day just what was going on.

When the reprints of the Board's first report (the Preliminary Note) came, he made up a mailing list which was quite long and then asked several of us to help him prepare them for mailing. There were several corrections to be made on the reprints and the notation "Compliments of the writers," all of which he did in his own handwriting while the rest of us addressed envelopes, put on postage stamps, and so forth. He should have sent them out under the franking privilege but he did not do so. I still have the rare and valuable copy (with his notations in ink) which he gave me at that time.

CHAPTER FOURTEEN

ADIOS CUBA—
WALTER REED'S DEATH

IN A previous chapter, my departure from Columbia Barracks for dusty as Post Surgeon at Rowell
Barracks was noted. The composition of the command,
the location of the post and conditions found there
were briefly related but there were important developments regarding mosquito control which are of
interest. By virtue of existing orders, I was not only
the surgeon of the post but also sanitary inspector of
the city of Cienfuegos. My assistants at the post were
Contract Surgeons H. M. James and J. M. Wheate.

Colonel Ezra P. Ewers of the Tenth Infantry was in
command, and he promptly gave his full support to
the mosquito control work I had proposed. The
problem was not difficult since the natural drainage
was excellent and the occupied area of the small command was not very large. The prevailing mosquitoes
were *A. aegypti* and *Culex pungens;* both were plentiful. A few marshy areas were found and they evidently
provided the anopheline mosquitoes which kept up

the malaria rate. These places were promptly ditched
and drained by post labor, and the hospital sanitary
squad began systematic oiling of every place where
standing water was found. With the fine piped water
supply and an excellent sewerage system which removed all waste water to the sea, I expected immediate
control of the mosquito problem. At the end of the
first month, we still had *A. aegypti*, but found no
anopheline mosquitoes. This was very perplexing for I
knew that the breeding places must be nearby and yet
none could be found. All at once, however, the problem was solved. Lining the walks from one end of the
post to the other were several hundred obsolete artillery shells from the old Spanish fort. They made an attractive border along the walks, being placed upright
at regular intervals. They were about a foot long with
three-quarters inch hole in the top. After rains, they
all contained water and the presence of larvae and eggs
was promptly demonstrated. A very simple method to
solve this problem was found. The holes were plugged
with corks obtained at the Post Exchange where an unlimited supply, extracted from soft drink and beer
bottles, was available. From that time on, we had no
mosquito problems for our systematic oiling and draining work had practically eliminated the breeding
places of anopheline mosquitoes. Malaria had been the
prevailing disease at the post since its establishment

as heretofore stated. Our results were so unexpectedly successful that they were noted by the Chief Surgeon, Department of Havana; and by General Wood.[30]

With the acquisition of our recent knowledge of the propagation of malarial fevers, it may be taken for granted that this preventable disease will be hereafter greatly reduced and, at most posts, practically eliminated. As an instance: for the week ending June 23, 1900, there were 34 cases of malarial fever under treatment at Rowell Barracks, Cuba (Cienfuegos). A year afterward, for the week ending June 22, 1901, chiefly in consequence of sanitary measures promoted by the Post Surgeon, Lieutenant A. E. Truby, there was not a single case.

Strangely enough, I had never seen this report until 1938 when I began to review the old reports for the preparation of this story. Colonel Havard evidently did not know that the credit for this work really belonged more to Reed than to me. He had taught me all that I knew about mosquitoes. His work had inspired me and made me confident that mosquito-borne diseases could be controlled. This splendid opportunity to demonstrate his ideas was given me and it was a pleasure to carry out his advice to the best of my ability. It was most inspiring to note the prompt success of our work.

[30] Annual Report of General Leonard Wood to the Secretary of War, June 30, 1901, p. 10.

For my duties as Sanitary Inspector of the city of Cienfuegos, a desk was provided for me in the city office of the Depot Quartermaster and I made such trips by boat as were necessary to run that office and keep in touch with Health Department affairs. The Alcalde and the local "medicos" were co-operative, just as they had been during my service at Guanajay. Nothing had yet appeared in the local papers about the Reed Board's mosquito experiments and the doctors could not be instilled with any of my enthusiasm for the theory. However, at my insistence, they consented to the screening of fever cases. The city depended mainly on rain water, and the many cisterns and other receptacles used for storing it made mosquito control a major engineering problem. Our efforts in that direction probably accomplished very little until April 17, 1901, when instructions from Headquarters, Department of Cuba, increased the authority of the Medical Inspector, and the Military Governor instructed the Alcalde of Cienfuegos to co-operate (Appendix VIII). By this time the results of the yellow fever experiments at Camp Lazear were generally known throughout Cuba and better co-operation was experienced. All fever cases were screened but satisfactory control of mosquito breeding in the city required more funds than ever were available in my time. However, much was accomplished by mosquito brigades.

During my tour of duty, the city had occasional cases of yellow fever but no epidemic. No cases occurred at the post. The first sanitary order issued by the Department of Cuba, requiring mosquito control and the screening of fever cases in military commands, had been issued December 21, 1900 (G. O. No. 6).* Such work was, however, in full operation at Columbia Barracks in October 1900 and at Rowell Barracks in December 1900 before General Order No. 6 was published.

Ordinary mosquito bars placed over the Quartermaster cots were not a huge success. Men did not like them for they were hot as they definitely obstructed the circulation of air, soon became torn and soiled, and were rarely properly tucked under the mattresses. To enforce the regulations about their use, inspection of sleeping quarters had to be made at night. The next morning, another careful inspection would usually show that, even in companies where regulations were well observed, a few mosquitoes with their bodies filled with blood could be found inside some of the nets. Furthermore, if parts of a naked body touched the side of the bar, the mosquitoes on the outside would certainly be there in force. Consequently a more satisfactory device had to be found for hospitals where mosquito-borne diseases were being treated. Very few

* Appendices V, VI, VII.

of the hospitals in Cuba had screened wards. Consequently, early in 1901, instructions were received at all military hospitals to provide screened cages with a screened vestibule for use in wards for the treatment of such cases. They were a great success, being practical, economical, and most efficient. They were large enough to hold two beds. A photograph of the frame gives a good idea of its construction.

After several weeks, a squadron of the Second Cavalry relieved the Tenth Infantry. Lieutenant Colonel E. D. Dimmick was in command. Dr. Wheate had been relieved but Dr. James and I were still on duty at the station. Early in 1902, Contract Surgeon C. E. Bruhl relieved James who went to Matanzas for duty.

The hospital was located on the hill back of Headquarters. It was well planned and met all of our requirements. The health of the command was exceedingly good. Troops frequently went on long practice marches and one of the medical officers always went along. Major Walter S. Schuyler of the Second Cavalry relieved Colonel Dimmick and became one of my good friends. He was always happy if he could be out with troops on long marches and he usually took me along. On February 10, 1902, with two troops of Cavalry and enough of the pack train to carry all of the equipment and baggage, we left the harbor on a large Quartermaster lighter and landed the next day at Jucaro. From there we marched back through Ciego de Avila, Sancti Spiritus, Tunas, and Trinidad. Sancti Spiritus was the most ancient in appearance of all the cities in Cuba that I had seen, with streets that were mere alleyways, paved with enormous cobblestones. The sanitary conditions of this place were in a most deplorable condition, and the local hospital which I visited was not too good, but the town itself was unique and interesting because of its apparent age. Trinidad also seemed old with stone houses and cobblestone streets and a railroad track running to a small harbor at Casilda some miles away to the south. Trinidad had been a thriving and very wealthy sugar center at one time but during one of the Cuban revolutions, the industry had been entirely destroyed and the city was practically abandoned. Large substantially built homes were vacant and we stopped to inspect the interiors of several of them, especially the most magnificent one, which had belonged to one of the most prosperous of the local magnates. Beautiful balustrades and walls decorated with some of the choice hard woods of Cuba were still in good condition. Beautiful inlay work was, however, falling to pieces from the dampness, for nearly all doors and windows were gone. We saw a few natives working in a sugar field outside of the town.

The trip was made during the dry season and was most interesting and delightful. Our camp at Sancti Spiritus was in a vacant lot in the center of the town and there, I think, we picked up a few cases of malaria, I being one of the victims even though I always used a mosquito bar most faithfully. A few days after returning to the post, I began to feel bad while doing my morning work at the hospital. My only assistant had gone away with the other half of the command on another practice march. At noon, I had a chill, sent for the Hospital Steward, and had him bring the medicines I wanted and slides for making blood smears. We made the smears and I saturated myself with quinine. In a day or two I was able to stain the specimens and find the parasites. My experience with malaria had been extensive and I was determined to prevent a recurrent attack. This I managed to do by the daily use of quinine and enormous doses on every occasion whenever I was under pressure. On a trip to New York a few months later, I took quinine to the physiological limit when I landed and again on my return to Cuba a month later. The experience of patients who had not carried out my instructions had taught me the importance of this precaution and I intended that the parasites in my system should meet their doom as soon as they freed themselves from their hiding places. They did.

On April 30, 1902, the squadron of the Second

Cavalry at Rowell Barracks was ordered to Fort Ethan Allen, Vermont, and sailed from Cienfuegos on the S. S. *Santiago* of the Ward Line, reaching New York on May 9. I was directed to proceed with them, being relieved at the post by Lieutenant J. L. Bevans, M. C., who came with an Infantry command to relieve the Second Cavalry. My service in Cuba had been pleasant, exciting and most valuable from a medical military standpoint but the order to return to home soil was most welcome. The best of the local people were at the dock to see us sail, and we said *"adios"* to them and to Cuba.

At Fort Ethan Allen, orders assigning me to Fort Wadsworth, Staten Island, New York, were received, and so, after serving nearly three and one-half years in Cuba, I was back in my native state. Major Walter D. McCaw was the post surgeon at my new station and he invited me to live and mess with him. He had a most remarkable memory and could quote from the gems of literature without hesitation. He was most brilliant and entertaining. His advice enabled me at that time to reach a decision about remaining in the Service and I began to prepare for the promotion examination which was soon to come. Major George F. Barney, Coast Artillery Corps, was also a member of the mess at McCaw's quarters where one of those old, well-trained Chinese cooks served us so well.

We were all bachelors and on Saturday afternoons, the three of us went to the city, had dinner and then attended the best "gay nineties" shows that were still going in full swing. It was all a great and most agreeable change for me.

In August I was surprised to receive an order to proceed to West Point, New York, for duty. I reported there on August 12 and found a most active service awaiting me. Major James D. Glennan was the Post Surgeon and he ran the Cadet Hospital. Captain A. N. Stark had recently arrived there from Cuba and ran the Soldiers' Hospital, did all the surgical work at both hospitals as well as the outpatient service which was very extensive. He had a junior assistant who was about to be relieved and Stark had asked for me to take his place. Strangely, Major Glennan was soon relieved by Colonel Valery Havard, thus bringing together again, after long service in Cuba, the three of us who had so much in common to discuss.

On October 22 I was sent to the Army General Hospital at Washington Barracks, D. C. for six weeks to enable Lieutenant James R. Church, M. C. to take my place and assist in coaching the Cadet football team. "Bob" Church had been a star player on the Princeton team during his college days. While I was at Washington Barracks, Major Walter Reed was admitted to the hospital with appendicitis.

Major William C. Borden, Medical Corps, performed the operation assisted by Lieutenant J. H. Ford and Lieutenant Clarence Connor. Surgeon General O'Reilly, Major J. R. Kean, Dr. Neff, Captain F. P. Reynolds, and I were among the few present to see the operation. Each night after the operation, a junior medical officer was constantly on duty with the patient and I was one of them. Peritonitis developed and at 2:05 A.M. on Sunday, November 23, 1902, Walter Reed passed away.

"His death in the prime of his life, in the zenith of his distinguished career, was a severe blow to scientific medicine, to his corps, and to the medical profession which he adorned." [31] But, as General McCaw said, "It is gratifying to think that, although his country and the scientific world were deprived of one from whose future services more benefit to humanity might reasonably be expected, nevertheless he was privileged before his life's close to know that his discovery had been tested, and that a great city was freed from her ancient foe, to know that his conscientious work had contributed immeasurably toward the future prospects of an infant republic and even more to the welfare of his own beloved country, whose flag he had served so faithfully." [32]

[31] District of Columbia, Medical Society Memorial Resolutions. Senate Document No. 822, 61st Congress, p. 33.

[32] Senate Document No. 822, 61st Congress, p. 13.

The military funeral on November 25, at St. Thomas' church, in Washington, was attended by a large number of friends, high officials of the government, general officers, members of the diplomatic corps, and distinguished men of the medical profession. Among them I saw Mr. Elihu Root, the Secretary of War, and Professors William H. Welch, William Osler, and Simon Flexner. Many officers of the Army, Navy, and Marine Hospital Services were present, as were the faculty and students of the Army and Navy Medical Schools and of Columbia College.

Walter Reed's remains were interred at Arlington Cemetery. On his monument is inscribed the following epitaph, derived from the remarks of President Eliot when Harvard University conferred the honorary degree of M.A. upon him in 1902:

"He gave to man control over that dreadful scourge, Yellow Fever."

APPENDIX

APPENDIX

I *

HEADQUARTERS 8TH INFANTRY

On Board S.S. *Florida*, in Havana Harbor, Cuba

December 15, 1898

GENERAL ORDERS

NO.   19

1. By direction of the Major General Commanding the Division the following order is published for the information and guidance of the command.

All canteens will be filled with water or coffee before leaving the ship.

Pending the construction of permanent water works, for which all the materials have not yet arrived, the camp will depend on wells for water, and the supply is limited, therefore the greatest care will be taken to see that no water is wasted.

2. No passes will be granted to any officer or enlisted man, to visit Havana except under orders. No one will be allowed to enter any house or liquor store in Marianao unless ordered to do so, nor will any soldier be allowed to go to the Playa de Marianao unless sent by the proper authority.

All officers are enjoined to enforce a strict compliance

* See page 19.

of the order issued to preserve the health of the command.

The Regimental Quartermaster is authorized to purchase the necessary amount of ground lime for disinfecting the sinks, pending the arrival of the Division Quartermaster, and all sinks will be sprinkled with fresh lime every two hours between reveille and tattoo.

By order of Lieut. Colonel Ellis:

F. H. SARGENT

1st Lieut. and Adjutant 8th Infantry
Adjutant

II *

HEADQUARTERS 8TH INFANTRY

CAMP NEAR MARIANAO, CUBA

December 17th, 1898

GENERAL ORDERS

NO.   20

1. Immediately after making use of any sink within the limits of this camp, each officer, soldier and employe will cover with loose earth his own excrement, and to this end boxes or mounds of loose dry earth with shovels, will be placed in each and every sink.

2. The officer of the day will inspect all sinks and pits of the regiment in the early morning, about the middle of the afternoon, and late in the evening, and will order

* See page 19.

a non-commissioned officer, of any company whose sinks are found to be improperly cared for, to cover and police them as ordered herein. He will also see that lime is freely used as directed in orders.

This will not relieve company commanders from making similar inspections as required by Army Regulations.

Any neglect observed to keep the sinks and pits as odorless as possible, or any inability to keep them so on account of want of lime, or other remedial causes, will be at once reported to the Regimental Commander.

The officer of the day will note on the guard report the hours at which he visited the sinks, with such remark as to their condition and his action as he may have to add.

By order of Lieut. Colonel Ellis:

F. H. SARGENT

1st Lieut. 8th Infantry Adjutant
Surgeon

III *

HEADQUARTERS COLUMBIA BARRACKS

COLUMBIA BARRACKS, CUBA
September 19, 1900

SPECIAL ORDERS

NO.   149

EXTRACT

1. First Lieutenant A. E. TRUBY, Assistant Surgeon, U. S. Army, having reported for duty at this post in

* See page 107.

TABLE III.

INOCULATION OF NONIMMUNE INDIVIDUALS THROUGH THE BITE OF MOSQUITOS (CULEX FASCIATUS).

NO. OF CASE.	AGE.	NATIVITY.	DATE OF INOCULATION.	CHARACTER AND NUMBER OF ATTACK AND NUMBER OF PATIENTS BITTEN.	DAY OF DISEASE.	TIME BETWEEN INFECTION OF MOSQUITO AND INOCULATION.	NO. OF MOSQUITOS.	RESULT.	REMARKS.
1		United States.	August 11.	Mild, 1.	Seventh.	5 days.	One.	Negative.	
2		United States.	" 11.	Very mild, 1.	Fifth.	5 "	One.	"	
3	24	United States.	" 12.	" " 1.	Fifth.	6 "	One.	"	
4	20	United States.	" 12.	" " 1.	Fifth.	6 "	One.	"	
5	24	United States.	" 14.	" " 1.	Fifth.	8 "	One.	"	
6	24	United States.	" 16.	" " 1.	Fifth.	10 "	One.	"	
7	22	United States.	" 18.	Severe, 1.	Second.	3 "	One.	"	
8	20	United States.	" 19.	Very mild, 1.	Fifth.	18 "	Two.	"	
9	28	United States.	August 23.	Severe, 1.	First.	3 "	One.	Negative.	
				Fatal, 1.	Second.	6 "			
				Mild, 1.	First.	4 "			
				Severe, 1.	Second.	2 "			
10	46	England.	August 27.	Severe, 1.	Second.	12 "	One.	Positive.	Severe attack of yellow fever.
				Mild, 1.	First.	6 "			
				Severe, 1.	Second.	4 "			
				Mild, 1.	Second.	2 "			
11	24	United States.	August 31.	Fatal, 1.	Second.	12 "	One.	Positive.	Well-marked attack of yellow fever.
				Mild, 2.	Second.	4 and 10 "			
				Severe, 2.	Second and ninth.	2 and 8 "			
				Severe, 3.	First, second and second.	2, 8 and 16 "			
				Mild, 2.	First and second.	6 and 10 "	One.		
				Fatal, 1.	Second.	12 "			
				Severe, 1.	First.	2 "	One.		
				Mild, 3.	First, second and second.	4, 6 and 10 "			
				Severe, 3.	All on first.	2, 4 and 8 "	One.		
				Mild, 1.	Second.	6 "			

compliance with Paragraph 3, Special Orders No. 44, Headquarters Department of Western Cuba, dated September 17, 1900, is assigned to duty as Post Surgeon, relieving Acting Assistant Surgeon A. S. PINTO, U. S. Army,

By order of Colonel Baldwin:

H. S. SICKEL

Captain & Adjutant, 7th U. S. Cavalry
Adjutant

IV *

TABLE III

There is every probability that Dr. Lazear was one of the first two listed cases in Table III.

Cases No. 3 and 5 (24 years of age) suggest that one or both of them might have been Private Dean as that was his age at that time.

Nos. 4, 7 and 8 remain undetermined.

No. 6 was Lazear and was so reported in the "Preliminary Note."

No. 9 was Dr. Pinto.

No. 10 was Dr. Carroll.

No. 11 was Private Dean (XY)

The photostat copy of Table III was made from the original reprint of the article in the *Philadelphia Medical Journal*, October 27, 1900, which Major Reed personally presented to the author.

* See pages 108, 118.

V *

HEADQUARTERS DEPARTMENT OF WESTERN CUBA

QUEMADOS, *October 15, 1900*

CIRCULAR NO. 8

The following communication from the Chief Surgeon is published for the information and guidance of Commanding Officers in this Department. The necessary action will be taken as therein recommended.

CHIEF SURGEON'S OFFICE
HEADQUARTERS DEPARTMENT OF WESTERN CUBA

QUEMADOS, CUBA, *October 13, 1900*

To THE ADJUTANT GENERAL OF THE DEPARTMENT

SIR: I have the honor to invite your attention to the following facts and their bearing on the health of the command:

The rôle of the mosquito in the transmission of certain diseases is now well established. The evidence is now perfect and conclusive that malaria, as well as filarial infections are carried by this insect, and there are reasons to suspect that it may be connected with the transmission of yellow fever also.

Every consideration of prudence, as well as comfort, demands therefore the protection of the commands at all posts. It is believed that this can be done with

* See pages 142 and 206.

a very slight expenditure of time and trouble by the enforcement by post commanders of two precautions namely:

1. The enforcement of the use of mosquito bars in all barracks and especially in all hospitals.

2. The destruction of the larvae or young mosquitoes, commonly known as "wiggletails" or "wigglers" by the use of petroleum on the water where they breed. The mosquito does not fly far and seeks shelter when the wind blows; so that it is usually the case that every community breeds its own supply of mosquitoes, in water barrels, fire buckets, or undrained puddles, post holes etc. An application of one ounce of kerosene to each fifteen square feet of water surface, once a month, will destroy not only all the young but the adults, who come to lay their eggs. The water in any cistern or tank is not affected in the least for drinking or washing purposes, if only it is drawn from below and not dipped out. For pools or puddles of a somewhat permanent character, draining or filling in is the best remedy. It is recommended that the medical officer who makes the sanitary inspections at each post be charged with the supervision of the details of these precautions.

Very respectfully, your obedient servant

J. R. KEAN
Major and Surgeon, U. S. V. Chief Surgeon

By command of Brigadier General Lee
R. E. L. MICHIE, *Assistant Adjutant General*

VI *

HEADQUARTERS DEPARTMENT OF CUBA

ORDERS, BOOKS, BLANKS & D. C. DIV.
REC'D DEC. 31, 1900
ADJUTANT GENERAL'S OFFICE

GENERAL ORDERS
NO.   6

HAVANA, *December 21, 1900*

The Chief Surgeon of the Department having reported that it is now well established that malaria, yellow fever and filarial infection are transmitted by the bites of mosquitoes, the following precautions will, upon his recommendation, be taken for the protection of the troops against the bites of these insects:

1. The universal use of mosquito bars in all barracks and especially in all hospitals, and also in field service when practicable.

2. The destruction of the larvae or young mosquitoes, commonly known as "wiggletails" or "wigglers" by the use of petroleum on the water where they breed.

The mosquito does not fly far and seeks shelter when the wind blows; so it is usually the case that each community breeds its own supply of mosquitoes in water barrels, fire buckets, post holes, old cans, cesspools, or undrained puddles.

An application of one ounce of kerosene to each fifteen square feet of water, twice a month, will destroy not

* See pages 187, 206.

only all the young, but the adult females who come to lay their eggs. The water in cisterns or tanks is not affected for drinking or washing purposes when not dipped out.

For pools or puddles of a somewhat permanent character, draining or filling up is the best remedy.

The Medical Department will furnish oil for the purpose above mentioned.

Post Commanders will carefully carry out these precautions.

By command of Major General Wood:

H. L. Scott

Adjutant General

VII *

HEADQUARTERS DEPARTMENT OF CUBA

Havana, *April 27, 1901*

CIRCULAR

NO. 5

Upon the recommendation of the Chief Surgeon of the Department, the following instructions are published and will be strictly enforced at all military posts in this Department:

The recent experiments made in Havana by the Medical Department of the Army having proved that yellow fever, like malarial fever, is conveyed chiefly, and probably exclusively, by the bite of infected mosquitoes, im-

* See pages 184, 205, 206.

portant changes in the measures used for the prevention and treatment of this disease have become necessary.

1. In order to prevent the breeding of mosquitoes and protect officers and men against their bites, the provisions of General Orders No. 6, Department of Cuba, December 21, 1900, shall be carefully carried out, especially during the summer and fall.

2. So far as yellow fever is concerned, infection of a room or building simply means that it contains infected mosquitoes, that is, mosquitoes which have fed on yellow fever patients. Disinfection, therefore, means the employment of measures aimed at the destruction of these mosquitoes. The most effective of these measures is fumigation, either with sulphur, formaldehyde or insect powder. The fumes of sulphur are the quickest and most effective insecticide but are otherwise objectionable. Formaldehyde gas is quite effective if the infected rooms are kept closed and sealed for two or three hours. The smoke of insect powder has also been proved very useful; it readily stupefies mosquitoes, which drop to the floor and can then be easily destroyed.

The washing of walls, floors, ceilings and furniture with disinfectants is unnecessary.

3. As it has been demonstrated that yellow fever cannot be conveyed by fomites, such as bedding, clothing, effects and baggage, they need not be subjected to any special disinfection. Care should be taken, however, not to remove them from the infected rooms until after formaldehyde fumigation, so that they may not harbor infected mosquitoes.

Medical officers taking care of yellow fever patients need not be isolated; they can attend other patients and associate with non-immunes with perfect safety to the garrison. Nurses and attendants taking care of yellow fever patients will remain isolated, so as to avoid any possible danger of their conveying mosquitoes from patients to non-immunes.

4. The infection of mosquitoes is most likely to occur during the first two or three days of the disease. Ambulant cases, that is, patients not ill enough to take to their beds and remaining unsuspected and unprotected, are probably those most responsible for the spread of the disease. It is therefore essential that all fever cases should be at once isolated and so protected that no mosquitoes can possibly get access to them until the nature of the fever is positively determined.

Each post will have a "reception ward" for the admission of all fever cases and an "isolation ward" for the treatment of cases which prove to be yellow fever. Each ward shall be made mosquito-proof by wire netting over doors and windows, a ceiling of wire netting at a height of seven feet above the floor, and mosquito bars over the beds. There should be no place where mosquitoes can seek refuge, not readily accessible to the nurse. Both wards can be in the same building, provided they are separated by a mosquito-tight partition.*

5. All persons coming from an infected locality to a

* It was soon found that the screening of hospital wards was not practicable at most stations in Cuba so the screened cages mentioned on page 207 were substituted.

post shall be kept under careful observation until the completion of five days from the time of possible infection, either in a special detention camp or in their own quarters; in either case, their temperature should be taken twice a day during this period of observation so that those who develop yellow fever may be placed under treatment at the very inception of the disease.

6. Malarial fever, like yellow fever, is communicated by mosquito bites and therefore is just as much of an infectious disease and requires the same measures of protection against mosquitoes. On the assumption that mosquitoes remain in the vicinity of their breeding places, or never travel far, the prevalence of malarial fever at a post would indicate want of proper care, and diligence on the part of the Surgeon and Commanding Officer in complying with General Orders No. 6, Department of Cuba, 1900.

7. Surgeons are again reminded of the absolute necessity, in all fever cases, to keep, from the very beginning, a complete chart of pulse and temperature, since such a chart is their best guide to a correct diagnosis and the proper treatment.

By command of Major General Wood:

H. L. SCOTT
Adjutant General

VIII *

HEADQUARTERS DEPARTMENT OF CUBA

HAVANA, CUBA
April 17, 1901

THE COMMANDING OFFICER
ROWELL BARRACKS, PASA CABALLOS, CUBA

SIR:

The Department Commander directs that the surgeon stationed at your post shall act as Medical Inspector of the town of Cienfuegos and its seaport, provided the seaport is not under the supervision of an officer of the Marine Hospital Service. He shall advise the Commanding Officer on all matters arising there which are liable to involve the health of the troops. His chief duties as Medical Inspector shall be:

1. To keep himself informed of the sanitary condition of the town and seaport and to make such special investigations and recommendations as he may deem necessary.

2. To inspect all hospitals in which fever cases are admitted, in order to ascertain the nature and number of these cases, and whether the provisions of Circular letter of March 5th, issued by the Superintendent of Charities, by order of the Military Governor, are being complied with.

3. To investigate the prevalence of mosquitoes, their

* See page 205.

species, the extent to which they produce malarial and yellow fever infections, the measures adopted to prevent their propagation, and the success thereof.

4. To ascertain what regulations (if any) are enforced regarding the examination of prostitutes, and their isolation and treatment when diseased.

5. On the last day of each month (or oftener if necessary), he will report to the Chief Surgeon of the Department, through the Post Commander, the cases of infectious diseases which occurred during the month in the town (and seaport), the general result of his inspections and investigations, and all other sanitary matters in which the health of the troops may be affected.

A copy of this communication has been furnished the Mayor of Cienfuegos with a letter (copy enclosed) which it is hoped will secure his full cooperation in the matter.

Very respectfully,

H. L. Scott
Adjutant General

OFFICE OF THE MILITARY GOVERNOR
ISLAND OF CUBA

Havana, Cuba
April 17th, 1901

The Alcalde, Cienfuegos, Cuba
Sir:

The Military Governor directs me to inform you that the Post Surgeon at Rowell Barracks, Pasa Caballos,

Cuba, has been appointed Medical Inspector of the town and seaport of Cienfuegos, with duties as outlined in the enclosed copy of communication to his commanding officer.

The Military Governor desires that during the coming summer the fullest medical and sanitary statistics of the Island be obtained and to that end asks that you kindly cooperate with the Medical Inspector detailed as above, giving him such assistance as lies in your power, in carrying out the instruction he has received.

Acknowledgement of this communication is requested.

Very respectfully,

H. L. SCOTT
Adjutant General

IX *

In 1905 Mr. Hans Schuler of Baltimore, Maryland, made an excellent white marble bust of Walter Reed. It was purchased from funds provided by the Walter Reed Memorial Association. The bust was loaned to the United States National Museum (Smithsonian Institution) and was on exhibition there, but in a location where it could not readily be seen by casual visitors.

In March 1935, the author being a member of the executive committee of the Walter Reed Memorial Association and also in command of the Army Medical Center, proposed that the Association have the bust trans-

* See Chapter XIII.

ferred to the Walter Reed General Hospital. The Army Medical Center was an administrative organization of a command which included the Walter Reed Hospital and the Army Medical, Dental and Veterinary Schools. The reservation consisted of forty-three acres of land near the northern boundary of the District of Columbia. This property was purchased in 1905 from a Congressional appropriation of $100,000 and the first buildings were constructed. In 1906 the War Department issued General Order No. 83 announcing the tract as a military reservation and directing that the new institution be known as the "Walter Reed General Hospital," thus "honoring the memory of the medical officer whose researches in yellow fever are by far the most important contributions to science which have ever come from an Army surgeon. In my judgement they are the most valuable contributions to medicine and public hygiene which have ever been made in the country with the exception of the discovery of anesthesia." [33]

It therefore seemed most appropriate to place the bust in the main lobby of this great memorial to Walter Reed and the Association authorized its transfer with the understanding that it be kept in the lobby of the hospital "unless and until some other disposition be made of it by the Association." The bust, on April 10, 1935, was placed in a niche prepared for it over the mantel of the fireplace as shown in the photograph in Figure 27.

[33] Letter of Professor William Welch of Johns Hopkins University to the Secretary of War. Senate Document No. 822, 61st Congress, p. 48.

INDEX

233

Paul B. Hoeber, Inc., Medical Book Department of Harper & Brothers, 49 East 33rd Street, New York